RANDOM VIBRATION

AN INTRODUCTION TO

Random Vibration

BY J. D. ROBSON

Senior Lecturer, School of Applied Dynamics
University of Edinburgh

EDINBURGH UNIVERSITY PRESS
Edinburgh
ELSEVIER PUBLISHING COMPANY
Amsterdam - London - New York
1964

United Kingdom
EDINBURGH UNIVERSITY PRESS

Commonwealth, except Canada
ELSEVIER PUBLISHING COMPANY LIMITED
12B, RIPPLESIDE COMMERCIAL ESTATE
RIPPLE ROAD, BARKING, ESSEX

United States and Canada
AMERICAN ELSEVIER PUBLISHING COMPANY, INC.
52 VANDERBILT AVENUE, NEW YORK 17, N.Y.

all remaining areas
ELSEVIER PUBLISHING COMPANY
335 JAN VAN GALENSTRAAT
P.O. BOX 211, AMSTERDAM

Printed in Great Britain by
Robert Cunningham and Sons Ltd
Alva, Scotland

PREFACE

Random vibration is essentially an engineering matter. It has developed into a recognisable subject because of the practical needs of industry, and the majority of those who study it do so because they wish to apply it to practical problems. It is the aim of this book, therefore, to make available to the reader a knowledge of the subject which will be of practical value to him.

In this subject however practical facility only becomes possible through a basic understanding of the subject as a whole, and it is this understanding which the book is primarily intended to facilitate. The basis of the subject is analytical and its presentation necessarily involves a good deal of mathematical analysis, but mathematics have been treated strictly as a means to an end and there are few concessions to rigour. Some attempt has been made to adjust the adequacy of any analytical argument to its value in assisting understanding, though it is difficult to be entirely consistent in this.

The level of mathematical proficiency assumed in the reader is that of an average honours graduate in engineering, taking into account that many approach the subject for the first time some years after graduation, with their mathematical facility a little impaired. (It is not, of course, suggested that only graduates are capable of benefiting from this book.) No previous knowledge of statistics or of harmonic analysis is assumed; most readers will have some familiarity with mechanical vibration, but an Appendix is provided in which the most important results and concepts of this subject are established.

The book is an 'Introduction' in the sense that it is designed to introduce. It is intended at once to provide a first introduction to those who have not previously encountered the subject, and also to provide the benefits of a proper introduction to those who have hitherto had a mere nodding acquaintance with it. But it has not been thought desirable to divide the book into elementary and advanced parts, and the subject is presented as a continuous whole.

The present work has developed from lectures given during postgraduate courses in the School of Applied Dynamics at Edinburgh University. Although it is not possible to make individual acknowledgement to all those who have helped in some way towards the completion of the book, I would like particularly to express my thanks to Professor R. N. Arnold and Professor L. Maunder who have read and commented on much of the text, to my father, Mr L. S. Robson, who has borne the brunt of the proof reading, and to Miss Marjorie Easson whose meticulous typing of the final draft has been a great help.

Edinburgh, *August* 1963

CONTENTS

CHAPTER I

INTRODUCTION

1.1 Random Vibration

Random vibration has become an important subject in recent years principally because of advances in high speed flight. It has become necessary to make structures and equipment which are capable of withstanding the randomly fluctuating loadings caused by the flow of turbulent air or the efflux from jet or rocket engines, and consequently a theory capable of analysing the effects of such loadings has been developed. But while the development of systems capable of high speed flight does offer a very suitable and important field for the application of the theory of random vibration, this theory is clearly capable of application in many other fields of engineering once the concepts and techniques have become more widely familiar.

When a theory of random vibration came to be developed it was not necessary to start from the beginning. Problems involving random processes had been studied previously in physics, where such matters as Brownian motion and statistical mechanics have been given a firm mathematical basis, and more recently in telecommunications and control systems, where a knowledge of the response of a system to a randomly varying input is of great importance because of the presence of unwanted noise along with all wanted signals. With a large literature available from these other fields it might seem that all the theory necessary to treat random vibration must already be available.

Certainly the basic concepts which are the foundation of all random process theory must be the basic concepts of random vibration analysis: the concepts necessary to describe the fluctuation of noise currents in a radio circuit must also be capable of describing the fluctuation of the pressure acting at a point on an aircraft wing. But in practice the application of the same basic theory to different types of problem does result in differences of emphasis and differences in preoccupation. In considering the response of control systems to random signals, for example, one is particularly interested in developing a system which will admit a wanted signal and discriminate heavily against unwanted noise. In random vibration our main interest is in knowing the effects on rather complex structures of random loadings whose distributions are often also of some complexity. So we are interested in aspects of the subject which are of little interest to those who work on control systems; we are not interested, on the other hand, in many of the topics treated in works whose intended application is to other fields.

In the present text therefore it is our object to isolate the ideas of the theory of random processes which are applicable to the problems of random vibration, and to show how, on this basis, a general theory of random vibration can be built up.

1.2 Characteristics of Random Vibration

In most vibration problems we are concerned to predict the motion of a system arising from a given force or forces. If a force varies harmonically, or periodically, or in a transient manner, or is completely describable in any other way as a function of time (and position), and if the initial position and motion of the system are known, techniques exist by which subsequent behaviour of the system can be completely predicted. And the response to a number of forces acting together may be obtained by superposition, at least where the system is linear. In many cases the response calculation need go no further than to establish that the applied force contains no harmonic components which are close to a natural frequency of the system.

But these techniques cannot be applied to the response of a system to a randomly varying force. It is essential to the nature of a random quantity that its value at any time t is not predictable in advance: it is essential to its nature also that any relationship between the magnitude of the quantity and time, measured during a certain time interval, will never exactly recur in any other. We are faced therefore with carrying out a calculation of response in which we cannot possibly know to what loadings the system will be responding. The familiar techniques of vibration analysis cannot begin to treat such a problem.

It is clear at once that we shall not be able to determine response in the usual precise sense: if we do not know the applied forces precisely we cannot expect to predict the response completely and express it as a function of time. It is clear also that we can make no progress at all until we have devised some way of describing a randomly

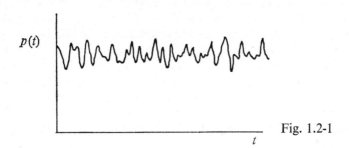

$p(t)$

t

Fig. 1.2-1

varying quantity; if we are not able to describe a quantity completely
we must describe it as completely as we can. We shall find in fact
that for a large class of random signals there exist methods of description by which we are not only able to describe a quantity as
completely as it is able to be described, but from which similar descriptions of related quantities can be determined. If we describe a
randomly varying applied loading as precisely as we are able, we can
in particular, knowing the properties of a system, give a similarly
precise description of the system's response. We shall find too that
such descriptions are quite sufficient for design purposes.

Analysis of random processes only becomes possible because many
physical quantities which vary in a random manner do exhibit a
degree of statistical regularity; they possess what we shall loosely
call stationary properties. Let us, to fix ideas, consider a specific
quantity – the pressure $p(t)$ at a certain point of an aircraft in flight.
In any particular flight this quantity can be measured and if plotted
against time will form a record as shown in Fig. 1.2-1. Although it
has no amplitude, no periodicity, and follows no apparent law, complete description of this quantity is certainly possible over the given
interval of time during which the record was made: the very act of
plotting it describes it. Outside this interval however it will never
repeat itself, and during the corresponding interval of any other
flight made under nominally identical conditions the record obtained
would not be the same. There is therefore little point in exact description. Provided however that the conditions of flight remained
the same, the record taken over any other interval would be expected
to be very similar in its general character: we should expect to find
for example that its mean value would remain the same, that its
spread about the mean value would be the same, that the number of

peaks per unit time would be the same, that the predominating frequencies, if any, would be the same. (All this is of course conditional on the interval of time considered being sufficient for these statistical parameters to be meaningful.) These are all quantities which are important in judging the probable effects of $p(t)$.

It would seem then that provided we are content with a description of a statistical nature, a quite useful description of a random process should not be impossible, at least if the mechanism by which it is generated remains unchanged over an adequate period of time.

1.3 Practical Applications

In developing the theory it is helpful to have in mind some idea of the types of problems with which we expect to have to deal in practice. In high speed flight we are principally interested in the ability of the vehicle – aircraft or rocket – to survive the loadings to which it is subjected: this means that we must be able to ensure that the stresses occurring in the structure are not sufficient to cause failure. Ideally then we must be able to determine the stresses arising in a structure from an expected random loading. This is no more than the problem of determining the motion of a system in response to given random excitation, because if the displacements are known the strains – and so the stresses – are determinable. (The loadings are often rather complicated, but often simplifying assumptions can be made.) Even when the stresses are known it may not be easy to obtain data as to the ability of the material to withstand them, but it is to be presumed that a better knowledge of material properties under random loading will eventually become available.

Apart however from the structural design problem it must be remembered that aircraft and rockets normally carry – and depend on – a great quantity of non-structural equipment. Electronic equipment, for example, may be essential to the control of a rocket, and its failure may lead to the failure of the whole equipment. But although electronic components can be made extremely rugged they cannot well be designed to withstand all the possible random motions which they might experience in service. Any inadequacies of this sort would indeed quickly become apparent in a flight test, but with a modern rocket an unsuccessful flight test proves inordinately expensive. There is considerable interest therefore in developing a test which will reproduce on the ground the motions which a vehicle will experience in flight and so enable both its own structure and its ancillary equipment to be proved before use. Here there is a need to describe (and reproduce) not just the variations of a single random quantity but the complete random motions of a particularly complex structure.

But application of random vibration theory is not restricted to the problems of high speed flight. Techniques applicable in this field are equally well applicable to an aircraft taxiing on an imperfect runway, or to the suspension of road vehicles travelling on an imperfect road. The behaviour of civil engineering structures subject to gust wind loading or to steady winds at high Reynolds numbers or seismic excitation; the behaviour of high precision gyroscopes with necessarily imperfect bearings; the behaviour of stabilised ships subject to wave motion; these are all random vibration phenomena which may be approached through an understanding of the concepts and analytical techniques which we shall introduce here.

1.4 The Nature of Random Vibration Theory

Obviously statistical analysis must play a large part in our consideration of random vibration problems. A great body of statistical theory has been developed over many years: its results are readily available and well tested, and if it is capable of describing, say, the distribution of heights among a population, it will be equally capable of describing the distribution of the values of a stress measured at successive instants of time.

But we shall find it necessary to combine statistical description with description based on the concepts of harmonic analysis, suitably generalised to make it applicable to continuous records such as that of Fig. 1.2-1. There are many occasions where the shape of a record is of more significance than its level distribution, and in such cases the methods of harmonic analysis provide the better description. In particular when we come to consider the response of a system to a randomly varying excitation, we shall see that a knowledge of the frequency content of the excitation makes it possible to make use of results obtained – experimentally or theoretically – for an excitation of discrete frequency. But those properties of a randomly varying quantity which we describe in terms of harmonic analysis can also be described in terms of statistics, and the availability of the two equivalent methods of describing the same properties is often a great convenience in analysis, where we can always work with the most suitable method for any particular purpose.

The basic ideas of statistics and harmonic analysis are therefore fundamental to our work on random vibration, and the next two chapters will be devoted to introducing the relevant ideas from these two fields of knowledge. In Chapter II we shall introduce the basic ideas of statistics and probability theory. In Chapter III we shall extend the usual ideas of harmonic analysis in accordance with our present needs, and introduce also the statistical equivalents of our harmonic descriptions.

So much is common to all random process theory. But a study of random vibration must be based also on the results and techniques of orthodox vibration theory: it is assumed that most readers will have some familiarity with this, but a brief account of the important ideas is given in the Appendix. (It need hardly be said that those who have no knowledge of the subject of vibration would be better advised to learn from a more complete account of the subject than from the Appendix: see for example references 2, 20, 24). The methods of normal mode analysis are particularly convenient for the consideration of the response of complex systems to random excitation. The response of systems due to single randomly varying forces is a relatively simple problem, and is considered in Chapter IV. But in practice it is often the case that many loads act together over the surface of a body, so that the response is dependent on the correlation between the loadings at the various points. The analysis of the response in such cases is considered in Chapter V.

In the last two chapters of the book the theory of random vibration developed in the previous chapters is applied to two practical problems: Chapter VI considers the basic problem of design – the prediction of the probability of failure of a component during a given service life – and Chapter VII considers the problem of simulating by means of a test a given random vibration environment.

1.5 Nomenclature, Notation, and Assumptions

Random vibration abounds in terms and concepts which are likely to be unfamiliar to most readers new to the subject. These must be made familiar because obtaining a clear understanding of them forms a large part of the work of understanding the subject. Fortunately the nomenclature is reasonably well standardised.

But notation, on the other hand, varies widely from author to author. Particularly for such important and continually recurring quantities as spectral density and autocorrelation function (which will be introduced in a later chapter) a great variety of symbols are to be found. Where it has been possible to find in the literature any tendency towards a common practice of usage the present text conforms: where this has not been possible, symbols have been chosen for their convenience from among those used elsewhere. Where possible, the notation has been made to be self explanatory by the consistent use of subscripts, etc. But throughout the book comprehensibility has been thought to be of more account than strict consistency, and composite symbols have been contracted where brevity is necessary for clarity, and expanded where there is a need to be more explicit.

Throughout this book it will be assumed that any random process with which we are concerned is such that its statistical characteristics do not vary with time; in fact that it is what is strictly called 'stationary and ergodic'. (The precise meaning of these two terms will be explained later, when statistical concepts have been introduced, but the idea is more important than the definition.) Such properties arc likely to be found whenever a randomly varying quantity results from steady conditions which do not change during a considerable period of time: this would be the case, for example, for an aircraft flying at constant speed through uniform atmospheric conditions. This may indeed often not be the case in practice, but allowance for time varying conditions can often be made if results for steady conditions are known. Theory based on the assumption of stationary and ergodic random processes bears much the same relationship to non-stationary conditions as a theory assuming linearity bears to a nonlinear system: linear theory is by no means irrelevant to the analysis of a physical world in which true linearity is very rare.

CHAPTER II

STATISTICAL ANALYSIS

2.1 Introduction

Let us consider a randomly varying quantity, denoted by $x(t)$, which may be any physical quantity such as force, or pressure, or stress, or acceleration: the independent variable t need not necessarily be time, though it may be convenient for the moment to consider it to be so. If this is recorded over an interval Δt the result may be represented as in Fig. 2.1-1. Although it is possible to plot $x(t)$

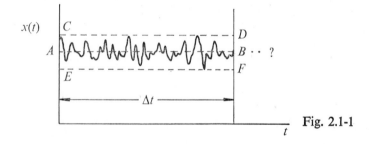

Fig. 2.1-1

against t for any particular interval Δt during which $x(t)$ has been measured, it is not possible to predict from this the precise value of $x(t)$ at any value of t outside the interval Δt.

But if we have reason to believe that the mechanism by which $x(t)$ is generated remains unchanged at all times, we can expect that the essential character of $x(t)$ outside Δt will remain unchanged also. Thus, for example, if the interval Δt is not too short $x(t)$ will have the same mean value (represented by AB) outside Δt as it does within it, and the extreme values of $x(t)$ will (except possibly very exceptionally) still lie between the limits represented by CD and EF. This technique of description is capable of considerable refinement, and by means of statistical concepts it is in fact possible to describe the essential features of the whole signal $x(t)$ with some precision on the basis of its behaviour in Δt. We can of course never hope to provide a complete description of a random process for if this were possible it would not be a random process.

Before developing such a technique for a quantity $x(t)$, it is helpful first to consider some rather more elementary statistical problems.

2.2 Probability

Statistical theory is based on the concept of *probability*. It might seem reasonable to begin by defining this concept firmly in general terms, but to do this presents considerable difficulty and it will not be attempted here. The measure of probability used is based on a scale such that the probability of the occurrence of an event which can not possibly occur is taken to be zero: the probability of the occurrence of an event which is absolutely certain to occur is taken to be unity. Any other event clearly must have a probability between zero and unity, although it may not be easy to see at once how any numerical value can be allotted to it.

In some cases an argument based on symmetry enables us to allot a precise measure of probability. Suppose that we spin a coin: we do not know beforehand whether to expect the result 'heads' or 'tails', but we can argue on grounds of symmetry that with a good coin the probability of the result 'heads' is equal to that of the result 'tails', or in symbolic form $\Pr[H] = \Pr[T]$. As the probability of 'either heads or tails', which will be equal to $\Pr[H] + \Pr[T]$, must be unity – for no other result is possible, at least in a well conducted experiment – it follows that $\Pr[H] = \Pr[T] = \frac{1}{2}$. Similarly we could argue that the probability of throwing any given number with a symmetrical six-sided die would be 1/6: all numbers from 1 to 6 are equally probable and their total probability must be unity.

Where no such argument as that of symmetry is available we have to base our measure of probability on the intuitively acceptable hypothesis that in any trial the probability of the occurrence of a particular event is equal to the relative frequency of its occurrence in a very large number of similar trials: if an event occurs in 500 out of a series of 1000 trials we assume that the probability of its occurring in any one trial is – at least approximately – equal to one-half. This assumption is easy to accept and leads to apparently sound results but it possesses obvious limitations as a basic definition. An attempt by the reader to confirm by experiment that the probability of the result 'heads' in a spin of a coin is exactly one-half will illustrate the difficulty, which is that the number of trials necessary to give a convincing result is very large indeed.

If we bear in mind the necessity for taking a sufficiently large sample before attempting to define probability, however, the empirical definition does prove satisfactory, and if there is any doubt as to the accuracy of a result it may even be possible to make some statistical estimate of the uncertainty involved.

Let us now consider the six-sided die a little further. If the die is perfectly made we can say before any given throw that the result will be a number N, which is equally likely to turn out to be any number between 1 and 6. The probability that N will be equal to 1 is equal to the probability that N will be equal to 2, and so up to 6, and the probability that N will turn out to have any particular one of these values is thus one-sixth. We can write therefore $\Pr[N=n]=1/6$ where n can be given any specified value from one to six: we can simplify this notation still further by writing $p(n) = \Pr[N = n]$ so that $p(n) = 1/6, (1 \leq n \leq 6)$; this can be plotted as a histogram against n (Fig. 2.2-1 (a)). The distinction between N and n should be noted: n represents any previously specified possible result while N is the previously unknown result of any trial. n can have any prescribed value: the value of N cannot be known (until after the trial) and we can only assess the probability of its having a particular value. We may note here the possibility of adding probabilities: the probability that N is odd is equal to $\Pr[N = 1$ or 3 or 5] which is equal to $p(1)+p(3)+p(5) = \frac{1}{2}$.

It is convenient here to define a further probability and to introduce a new symbol: $P(n) = \Pr[N \leq n]$; that is, the probability that N is not greater than any given number n. We see that, for example $P(4) = p(1)+p(2)+p(3)+p(4) = 2/3$. Indeed, it is always the case that $P(n) = \sum_{1}^{n} p(r)$, and if it is plotted against n, we obtain a uniform staircase as in Fig. 2.2-1(b). The quantities $p(n)$ and $P(n)$ provide alternative means of describing the distribution of probability between the various possible values of n. In what follows the term *probability distribution* will be used to denote the general properties of which the various defined quantities (e.g. $p(n)$) provide a quantitative description.

A further quantity which we shall use later is the *expectation*, $E(N)$. This is the expected result in any given trial, assumed to be equal to the mean result of a very large number of trials. In the case

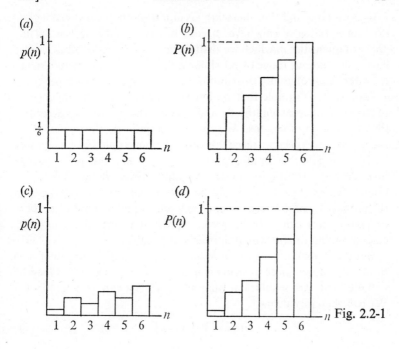

Fig. 2.2-1

of the symmetrical die we can assume that in many throws all the numbers from one to six will recur with equal frequency, so the expectation here is the mean of 1, 2, 3, 4, 5, 6, i.e.

$$E(N) = (1+2+3+4+5+6)/6 = 3\tfrac{1}{2}.$$

(This we could clearly write also as $\sum_1^6 n\,p(n)$.)

With a loaded die the probability distribution would be modified somewhat. We could no longer infer the values of $p(n)$ from symmetry, but an experiment consisting of a very large number of throws would indicate some such distribution as that shown in Fig. 2.2-1(c). If we were now to plot $P(n)$ the staircase would no longer be uniform but would be as shown in Fig. 2.2-1(d) with $P(n) = \sum_1^n p(r)$. The expectation would now be a weighted mean of the numbers 1 to 6, expressible only as $E(N) = \sum_1^6 n\,p(n)$, some numbers occurring with greater frequency than others.

In both coin and die, there are certain discrete values which the random variable N can have: a coin has two, a die has six. The physical quantities in which we shall be interested, on the other hand, have a continuous range of possible values. We must therefore next consider the probability distributions of quantities of this type.

Suppose for example that we have a very large number of pieces of string of different lengths, X, and suppose that we wish to describe the distribution of lengths. We could attempt to do this by defining the probability that any piece taken at random would have a certain length x, and do this for all possible lengths x. This operation would however be unhelpful, for no string could be *precisely*, say, 12 inches long. Clearly $\Pr[X = x]$ would be zero for *any* precise value of x; the probability of the occurrence of any one out of an infinite number of possibilities can only be zero. So the use here of a quantity corresponding to $p(n)$ would appear inapplicable.

But the probability – corresponding to $P(n)$ – that the length of the randomly chosen piece of string is less than a certain specified length *is* finite, and with a sufficient number of trials it can be determined. We can therefore define

$$P(x) = \Pr[X \leqq x] \tag{1}$$

without difficulty, and plot it with precision if a large enough number of trials can be made. This quantity is known as the *distribution function*, and it provides a precise quantitative description of the distribution of the lengths of all the pieces, or, because of our definition of probability, of the probability distribution associated with taking a single piece at random. If plotted against x it will in general give a continuous curve and in the present case will be somewhat like that shown in Fig. 2.2-2. This may be seen to conform to certain obvious physical conditions: the probability that any string will have a negative length is zero; the probability of a very small positive length is small; the probability that a string will have any given value x_1 must be less than one; almost all strings will be found to have lengths less than some suitable large positive value of x. The plot of $P(x)$ will be seen to embody all the information we can expect to know about the values of the quantities in our sample, and so of the probabilities of a single trial. It is possible however to plot the information in other ways.

As probabilities can be added, they can also be subtracted. We can thus deduce from the distribution function of Fig. 2.2-2 the

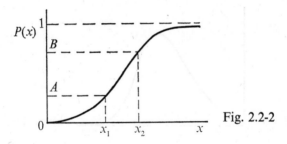

Fig. 2.2-2

probability of any randomly selected string having a length between two limits x_1 and x_2: this will of course be equal to the proportion of our very large number of pieces whose lengths are in this range. As

$$\Pr[x_1 \leqq X \leqq x_2] = \Pr[X \leqq x_2] - \Pr[X \leqq x_1],$$
$$= P(x_2) - P(x_1),$$

this probability is given by the length AB in Fig. 2.2-2.

This last result can be extended to give us a $p(x)$ which does in fact correspond closely to our previous $p(n)$. The probability that X lies between x and $x+dx$, which we can call $dP(x)$, can be obtained in the same way. Thus

$$dP(x) = \Pr[X \leqq x+dx] - \Pr[X \leqq x],$$
$$= P(x+dx) - P(x).$$

Now this probability, if dx is small enough, will be proportional to dx, and we can call it $p(x)dx$. We then have $dP(x) = p(x)dx$, which, when $dP(x)$ and dx become infinitesimal, reduces to the differential relation

$$p(x) = \frac{dP(x)}{dx}. \tag{2}$$

The quantity $p(x)$ is called the *probability density* and provides a second way of describing precisely the probability distribution of a random variable. When plotted it will have the form of Fig. 2.2-3: here the higher portions of the curve correspond to the region in which most values in the sample are found, corresponding to the region of greatest slope of $P(x)$, and the lower parts of the curve indicate values of x which occur only comparatively rarely.

Plots of both distribution function, $P(x)$, and probability density, $p(x)$, thus embody the identical facts concerning the probability

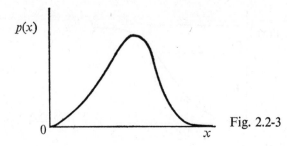

Fig. 2.2-3

distribution of a random variable, X, and either can be obtained if the other is known. We have defined $p(x)$ in terms of $P(x)$, and usually $P(x)$ is the easier to obtain experimentally, but the reverse process can be carried out by writing

$$P(x) = \int_{-\infty}^{x} p(z) \, dz. \tag{3}$$

For pieces of string the lower limit of the integration could be zero, but in general negative values of x will be possible, and all values of x must be covered by the $p(x)$ and $P(x)$ curves.

The shape of the $p(x)$ or $P(x)$ curves gives a qualitative indication of the nature of a distribution even without detailed quantitative interpretation. For example, a variable whose values were closely clustered about a mean would obviously give a tall narrow $p(x)$ curve or a $P(x)$ curve steeply rising near the mean value.

A word often used when referring to a statistical distribution is 'confidence'. Thus we might say that the declared life of a given component is based on a 95% confidence level. By this we would mean that 95% of a large number of components tested had a life in excess of this declared value. This would be equivalent to saying that any sample taken would have a probability of 0·95 of exceeding the declared value, or a probability of 0·05 of failure within the declared value. A confidence level then is simply a measure of probability and may be read off a curve giving the distribution function.

2.3 The Statistics of Random Processes

It has seemed best to introduce the basic ideas of statistics by considering random variables in which the trials and events have a clear physical existence. Let us now relate these ideas to the type of random process with which we are concerned in random vibration:

$x(t)$

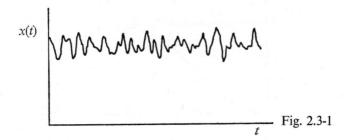

t

Fig. 2.3-1

the ideas to be presented will be perfectly general, but in approaching the subject it is convenient to fasten our ideas to some particular physical quantity.

Suppose that $x(t)$ (Fig. 2.3-1) represents the pressure acting at a given point of an aircraft flying through turbulent air; this will vary with time in a random manner, but if the conditions remain steady the character of the record will remain unchanged with time – it will be what we may loosely call 'stationary'. We can then generate a random variable of the 'piece of string' type by considering values of $x(t)$ at equal intervals of time, say one per second. These values will, if a sufficient length of record is available, give a sufficiently large sample for a probability distribution plot to be made, using the definition

$$P(x) = \Pr[x(t) \leq x] \qquad (1)$$

corresponding with 2.2(1). But clearly the same distribution would be obtained for a frequency of sampling of one per millisecond, or indeed for any other frequency of sampling whose interval is small in relation to the length of the record, and so in the limit $P(x)$ can be seen to be equal to the proportion of the total record length in which $x(t)$ is less than or equal to a certain level x. The way in which the magnitude of a quantity is distributed with respect to time is clearly an important practical consideration, and the equivalence of the probability distribution and the time distribution of such a function is an important property.

If we are interested in the actual value of a randomly varying quantity we can use the distribution function directly to define the probability that the magnitude will, at any given time, exceed a certain critical level x_1: if $P(x_1) = 0\cdot99$ then it is 99% probable that

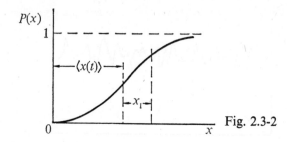

Fig. 2.3-2

$x(t)$ does not exceed x_1: over a long enough record, therefore, $x(t)$ spends only 1% of its time above the x_1 level.

We may however, as for example for the purpose of fatigue calculations, be interested in separating the steady and fluctuating components of our signal. The steady component is simply the mean value or the expectation $E[x(t)]$ of $x(t)$; we shall use angular brackets to indicate the time average of a quantity and so shall write this as $\langle x(t) \rangle$. This, by analogy with the die problem, is given by

$$\langle x(t) \rangle = \int_{-\infty}^{\infty} x\, p(x)\, dx. \tag{2}$$

(The expectation might be more easily obtained directly from the signal than by integration of $p(x)$: it could not however be easily obtained from $P(x)$ unless this happened to be symmetrical.) It will be seen from (2) that $\langle x(t) \rangle$ is given by the position of the centroid of the $p(x)$ diagram, since

$$\int_{-\infty}^{\infty} p(x)\, dx = 1.$$

With the mean value $\langle x(t) \rangle$ known, the properties of the fluctuating component are readily obtained from the distribution function by shifting the x origin through $\langle x(t) \rangle$: we can read off from the $P(x)$ curve the new distribution function $P(x_1)$ giving the probability that $x(t)$ shall be in the range $x(t) \leq \langle x(t) \rangle + x_1$. (See Fig. 2.3-2.) So we are well able to describe the probability distribution of a single randomly varying quantity.

But in considering such a quantity as the pressure on an aircraft we are not interested only in the properties of a single quantity $x(t)$ occurring during a single flight, but in those of all quantities

$x_1(t), x_2(t), x_3(t), \ldots$, etc., applying in all possible flights by identical aircraft under similar conditions. The ensemble of all such records $x_1(t), x_2(t)$, etc., is said to constitute a *random process*, and we must concern ourselves with the whole process. It is usual to denote the whole random process by $\{x(t)\}$, keeping $x(t)$ to denote a single member. Fortunately it is possible to convince ourselves that for our purposes the statistical properties of a single member function $x(t)$ do define the properties of the whole process $\{x(t)\}$.

The pressures $x_1(t), x_2(t)$, etc., obtained from flights made under identical conditions will not themselves be identical, but they will, taken together, have certain statistical properties in common. If the conditions prevailing during all flights are identical, and if moreover the conditions remain steady during each flight, we can in general assume that the process $x(t)$ is – in statistical language – both *stationary* and *ergodic*. By 'stationary' we mean that the probability distribution obtained by taking as variables the values of the quantities $x_1(t_1), x_2(t_1), \ldots$, etc., at any instant of time t_1 is independent of the choice of the instant t_1. By 'ergodic' we mean that the distribution of the quantities $x_1(t_1), x_2(t_1), \ldots$, at any one time is equal to the distribution with respect to time of any single member function of the random process.

So if we restrict our attention to stationary and ergodic random processes, as is justified for the type of randomly varying quantity with which we shall be concerned, it will be immaterial whether we consider the probability distribution of all member functions taken at any instant or the distribution with respect to time of any single member function: both will be identical. We can therefore, by determining the statistical properties of a single member function $x(t)$, define the statistical properties of the whole random process $\{x(t)\}$ of which $x(t)$ is a member. It will usually be convenient to determine the statistical properties of a random process in this way, and often more convenient to think only of the behaviour of a single randomly varying quantity rather than of the whole ensemble of functions which make up the process. It is also convenient to use the word 'stationary' not in the strict sense defined above, but to indicate the statistically regular behaviour of the single function $x(t)$ which we consider.

2.4 Variance

When there is a mean value this can always be found easily enough

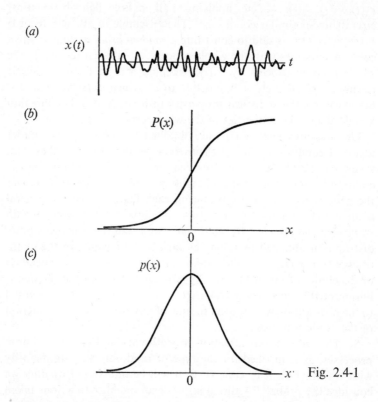

(a) $x(t)$

(b) $P(x)$

(c) $p(x)$

Fig. 2.4-1

and subtracted from the total signal: in considering the statistics of a random process therefore it is not only simpler but also realistic to consider only signals having zero mean value.

Suppose that a signal $x(t)$ has zero mean value: then it will give a record like that in Fig. 2.4-1(a). This will have a distribution function plot extending on both sides of the origin, and a probability density plot with its centroid directly above the origin (Fig. 2.4-1(b) and (c)).

To describe completely the nature of the spread of $x(t)$ on either side of the zero level would require the construction of one of these two plots. But the mean-square value of $x(t)$, i.e. $\langle x^2(t) \rangle$, does give an approximate measure of spread of a distribution: if this is small the $p(x)$ curve has a narrow peak and $P(x)$ is steep near $x = 0$. In the language of statistics the mean-square value is known as the *variance* of the particular $x(t)$ and is commonly denoted by σ^2. This makes the symbol σ available for the root-mean-square value, which is known as the *standard deviation* of $x(t)$.

If there is a mean value the variance is defined as the mean-square value of the difference from the mean value. Thus in this case

$$\sigma^2 = \langle [x(t) - \langle x(t) \rangle]^2 \rangle. \tag{1}$$

This expression can be simplified, by first expanding it:

$$\begin{aligned}\sigma^2 &= \langle x^2(t) - 2x(t) \langle x(t) \rangle + \langle x(t) \rangle^2 \rangle \\ &= \langle x^2(t) \rangle - 2\langle x(t) \rangle^2 + \langle x(t) \rangle^2 \\ &= \langle x^2(t) \rangle - \langle x(t) \rangle^2. \end{aligned} \tag{2}$$

This result emphasises the difference between $\langle x^2 \rangle$ and $\langle x \rangle^2$.

Where there is a mean value, we may well be interested in the magnitude of the spread in comparison with the size of the mean value. (This would be the case if our variance represented the mean-square error in some measured quantity.) We could then use a dimensionless variance defined as $\sigma^2 / \langle x(t) \rangle^2$.

It may be noted that just as $\langle x(t) \rangle$ is given by the first moment of area of the probability density curve about the $p(x)$ axis, so σ^2 which by (1) is the expectation of $[x(t) - \langle x(t) \rangle]^2$ is given by the second moment of area about $x = \langle x(t) \rangle$, i.e.

$$\sigma^2 = \int_{-\infty}^{\infty} [x - \langle x(t) \rangle]^2 \, p(x) \, dx. \tag{3}$$

As the probability density curve must have unit area, σ is in fact its 'radius of gyration' about $x = \langle x(t) \rangle$. If the mean value is zero the variance is given simply by

$$\sigma^2 = \int_{-\infty}^{\infty} x^2 \, p(x) \, dx. \tag{4}$$

2.5 Gaussian or Normal Distribution

The description of the statistical properties of a given random variable or process by distribution function $P(x)$ or probability density $p(x)$ will in general only be possible after the laborious analysis of a considerable number of results or records, although in the case of a random signal which is in – or can be converted into – electrical form, the work can be considerably shortened by the use of electronic devices. The distribution can in general be described only by an experimentally obtained curve which is not expressible by means of any mathematical expression. In such a case incorporation in mathematical analysis is not easy.

There are however several commonly occurring distributions which are expressible in mathematical form, and one of these, the Gaussian (or Normal) distribution is of particular importance because of its frequent occurrence in random vibration problems. It is found, for example, that loadings on aircraft usually conform closely to a Gaussian distribution, and it is also the case that the response of a linear system to a Gaussian excitation is itself Gaussian. We shall therefore be very closely concerned with Gaussian distributions.

A signal $x(t)$ or process $\{x(t)\}$ is said to be Gaussian if its probability density has the form

$$p(x) = \frac{1}{\sigma\sqrt{(2\pi)}}\, e^{-x^2/2\sigma^2}. \tag{1}$$

It is assumed here that the signal has zero mean value, as will be inferred from the symmetry of the distribution. The quantity σ^2 is the variance of $x(t)$, as the reader will be able to confirm by using 2.4(4) and carrying out the necessary integration. It is similarly possible to confirm that (1) satisfies

$$\int_{-\infty}^{\infty} p(x)\, dx = 1.$$

So if a signal is known to have a Gaussian distribution its probability density can be plotted immediately its variance is known: instead of by a laborious analysis of levels, the distribution can be completely specified by a single determination of the mean-square value. The distribution function corresponding to (1) is of course given by

$$P(x) = \int_{-\infty}^{x} p(z)\, dz = \frac{1}{\sigma\sqrt{(2\pi)}} \int_{-\infty}^{x} e^{-z^2/2\sigma^2}\, dz. \tag{2}$$

Curves showing the probability density and distribution function of a Gaussian distribution are plotted for various values of σ in Fig. 2.5-1(a) and Fig. 2.5-1(b). These curves can be made to apply where there is a mean value $\bar{x}$ simply by shifting the x origin. Thus in the general case:

$$p(x) = \frac{1}{\sigma\sqrt{(2\pi)}}\, e^{-(x-\bar{x})^2/2\sigma^2}. \tag{3}$$

The curves of Fig. 2.5-1 form a good example of the description

(a) $p(x)$

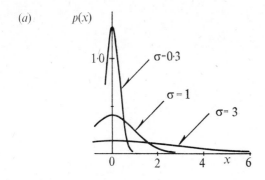

(b) $P(x)$

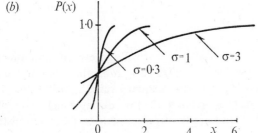

Fig. 2.5-1

of a probability distribution and show the kind of statistical information which is likely to be available about a random signal. We
can see how a small variance is characterised by a narrow probability
density curve and steep distribution function. Large variance on the
other hand is characterised by a broad probability density curve
indicating a great spread in the possible values of the random variable. In the extreme cases of $\sigma = 0$ and $\sigma = \infty$ the probability
density curve is confined to the line $x = 0$ and to the line $p(x) = 0$
respectively.

The significance of variance as applied to a signal with a Gaussian
distribution can be best appreciated by plotting the several curves of
Fig. 2.5-1(b) as a single curve: this can be done simply by plotting
$P(x)$ against x/σ instead of against x itself. This gives us Fig. 2.5-2.
From it we see that the probability that at a given time the magnitude
of $x(t)$ will not exceed the root-mean-square value of $x(t)$ is 0·68:
the probability that it will not exceed twice the root-mean-square

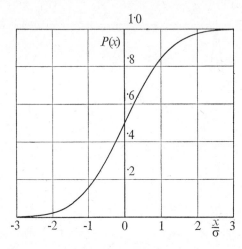

1·0

$P(x)$

·8

·6

·4

·2

-3   -2   -1   0   1   2 $\frac{x}{\sigma}$ 3

Fig. 2.5-2

value is 0·954: the probability that it will not exceed three times the root-mean-square value is 0·997: the probability that it will not exceed four times the root-mean-square value is 0·999936. These results also give the proportion of the time during which $x(t)$ remains below these levels: they apply of course only to Gaussian distributions and cannot be expected to apply to other distributions.

Tabulated values of the probability distribution function $P(x)$ (Equation (2)) for a Gaussian distribution are to be found in many books on statistics: see for example reference 7.

This integral is obviously closely related to the Gaussian error function,

$$\text{erf}\,\xi = \frac{2}{\sqrt{\pi}} \int_0^\xi e^{-t^2}\,dt \qquad (4)$$

which may also be found tabulated. (See e.g. Jahnke and Emde (reference 13)).

The derivation of $P(x)$ from erf ξ can be confusing and may be worth demonstrating. From (2)

$$P(x) = \frac{1}{\sigma\sqrt{(2\pi)}} \int_{-\infty}^x e^{-z^2/2\sigma^2}\,dz$$

$$= \tfrac{1}{2} + \frac{1}{\sigma\sqrt{(2\pi)}} \int_0^x e^{-z^2/2\sigma^2}\,dz,$$

because of symmetry.

Writing $z^2/2\sigma^2 = t^2$, therefore, we have

$$P(x) = \tfrac{1}{2} + \frac{1}{\sqrt{\pi}} \int_0^{x/\sigma\sqrt{2}} e^{-t^2}\, dt$$

(as $z = x$ when $t = x/\sigma\sqrt{2}$),

$$= \tfrac{1}{2}\left(1 + \mathrm{erf}\frac{x}{\sigma\sqrt{2}}\right). \qquad (5)$$

It can be shown, though we shall not prove it here, that a variable which is the sum of two or more Gaussian random variables has itself a Gaussian distribution.

2.6 Probability of a Single Event from Many Trials

We shall be interested eventually in determining the probability of failure of a component during its intended life, in order to ensure that this probability can be kept to a satisfactorily low level. To do this it is necessary to relate the probability of failure to the duration of the life of the component. There is clearly not a linear relationship because probability can never be greater than unity: if the probability of failure during a life of 100 hours is found to be 0·2, it cannot be the case that the probability of failure during a life of 1000 hours is 2·0. To establish the true relationship we must now consider the quantity 'expectation' in respect of trials whose outcome is restricted to 'success' or 'failure'. It will be convenient to explain this by referring again to the symmetrical six-sided die.

Expectation has been defined as the expected result of a given trial, assumed to be equal to the mean result of a large number of similar trials, and this was illustrated in Section 2.2 by considering a perfect six-sided die: as all numbers from 1 to 6 are equally probable, the mean score over many throws is $3\tfrac{1}{2}$, and the expectation for a single throw is therefore $3\tfrac{1}{2}$. In interpreting the definition here we have taken a 'trial' to consist of one throw, and the 'result' of the trial to consist of the score obtained. But there are other possible interpretations of the word 'trial' and of the word 'result', and so other possible expectations. For example, in some games in which dice are used it is necessary to throw a six in order to start. For this purpose the score is immaterial; what matters is the result and only two results are possible: 'success' or 'failure'. The expectation of success from a single throw would be one-sixth, because success would occur in one-sixth of any very large number of throws; the probability of success would also be one-sixth.

In the case of a single throw of a die the expectation of success is equal to the probability of success. But if we consider the result of a number of throws this is no longer so: the expectation of successes in throwing a six in six throws would be unity, being the average number of sixes which would be thrown in a very large number of trials, each consisting of six throws. But the probability of throwing a six in six throws cannot be unity; for this to be so would imply that to throw at least one six in every six throws is inevitable. The discrepancy is of course explained by the fact that although in some trials more than one six may be thrown, success can never be more than complete, so that the expectation of further sixes does not have a proportional effect on the probability of success.

Consider a series of trials in each of which the probability of the occurrence of a particular event is p. Then the expectation of its occurrence in each trial is also p, and the expectation, E, of occurrence in n trials is np. What we wish to know is the probability P of occurrence in n trials, which is not, evidently, equal to E.

The probability that the event will *not* occur in any one trial is $1-p$: the probability that it is completely absent from *all* of n trials is therefore $(1-p)^n$: thus the probability that the event will occur in the n trials, which is equal to the probability that it is not completely absent, must be given by

$$P = 1-(1-p)^n \tag{1}$$

This gives the probability of occurrence in a number of trials, when the probability of occurrence in a single trial is known. (We can, for example, now calculate that the probability of throwing a six with our die, given six attempts, is 0·663).

As p is always less than unity, equation (1) can be expanded by the binomial theorem in the form

$$P = 1-\left[1-np+\frac{n(n-1)}{2!}p^2 - \cdots\right]$$
$$= np-\frac{n(n-1)}{2!\,n^2}(np)^2 + \cdots. \tag{2}$$

If it happens that n is very large, we can write

$$P = np-(np)^2/2+(np)^3/6- \cdots,$$
$$= E-E^2/2+E^3/6- \cdots. \tag{3}$$

If it also happens that E is small this must reduce to

$$P = E, \text{ approximately.}$$

These results are applicable to the determination of the probability of failure of a component during its service life T. We shall in Chapter VI develop analysis from which we can easily determine the expectation of failure of the component in unit time: we shall denote this by E_1. (Here the event in which we are interested is failure, rather than success: this of course does not affect the argument).

Let us choose a time interval ΔT which is very small so that the probability of failure within it is equal to the expectation $E_1 \Delta T$. We can now regard the interval ΔT as a single trial, and treat the probability of failure within it as the p of the previous analysis. As the expectation of failure within the service life T is $E_1 T$, the probability of failure within the time T ($=n\Delta t$, where n is very large) can be determined from (3), as

$$P = E_1 T - \tfrac{1}{2} E_1{}^2 T^2 + \ldots \ . \tag{4}$$

In such a problem the expectation of failure within the service life is likely to be small; if this is so, nearly enough,

$$P = E_1 T. \tag{5}$$

2.7 Combined Probabilities

We have up to now considered the probability of the occurrence of a single event, or the probability distribution of a single quantity: for many problems of random vibration this is all that is required. But it is often essential to consider the combined probability of two or more events, or the probability distribution of a combination of two random signals. The concepts we have introduced can quite easily be extended to deal with such a case.

Where the results of two different trials, or the values of two randomly varying quantities, are quite unrelated, the combined probability is simply the product of the probabilities of the two separate events or values. The probability of two heads from successive spins of a coin is $\tfrac{1}{2} \times \tfrac{1}{2} = \tfrac{1}{4}$. The probability of throwing a one and a two – in that order – in successive throws of a symmetrical six-sided die is $1/6 \times 1/6 = 1/36$: if the die were loaded it would be $p(1) \times p(2)$, using our previous notation. The probability that a quantity $x(t)$ will find itself within the range $x \leq x(t) \leq x + dx$ and that

$y(t)$ will simultaneously find itself within the range $y \leqq y(t) \leqq y+dy$, if $x(t)$ and $y(t)$ are quite uncorrelated, is simply $p(x, y)\, dx\, dy = p(x)\, p(y)\, dx\, dy$, where $p(x), p(y)$ are probability densities as already defined. In this latter case $p(x, y) = p(x)\, p(y)$ is a two-dimensional probability density and it could be plotted as a surface above a horizontal xy plane: vertical sections parallel to the x and y axes would give curves proportional to $p(x)$ and $p(y)$.

When two separate variables $x(t), y(t)$, are not completely independent the combined probability density $p(x, y)$ is not a simple product and must in general be obtained as a function of x and y, in exactly the same way as $p(x)$ was obtained in terms of x. The joint probability distributions of applied force and the stress at a point, or of the displacements of two points on the same structure could not be expected to be independent. The joint distribution function $P(x, y)$ and joint probability density $p(x, y)$ for two variables are connected by a relationship analogous to that for a single variable. Now

$$p(x, y) = \frac{\partial^2 P(x, y)}{\partial x \partial y}, \tag{1}$$

and conversely

$$P(x, y) = \int_{-\infty}^{x} \int_{-\infty}^{y} p(\xi, \eta)\, d\xi\, d\eta. \tag{2}$$

(It still must be the case that $\displaystyle\int_{-\infty}^{\infty} \int_{-\infty}^{\infty} p(x, y)\, dx\, dy = 1$.)

In this case, the probability density of a function of two variables could still be plotted as a surface, but now cross-sections taken with one variable kept constant would no longer be similar in form.

The above results are extensible to any number of variables. The combined probability that $x(t), y(t), \ldots$, etc., are to be found in the ranges $x \leqq x(t) \leqq x+dx, \; y \leqq y(t) \leqq y+dy, \ldots$, etc., is expressible as $p(x, y, \ldots)\, dx\, dy \ldots$. Again if all the variables are independent this is expressible as $p(x)\, p(y) \ldots dx\, dy \ldots$: if the variables are not independent no such factorisation is possible. The joint probability density and the joint distribution function are related in the same way. In this case

$$p(x, y, \ldots) = \frac{\partial^n P(x, y, \ldots)}{\partial x \partial y \ldots}, \tag{3}$$

and $\qquad P(x, y, \ldots) = \displaystyle\int_{-\infty}^{x} \int_{-\infty}^{y} \ldots p(\xi, \eta, \ldots)\, d\xi\, d\eta \ldots$. (4)

The Gaussian probability distribution for a single variable, which we have considered earlier, has a multidimensional counterpart. Thus the distribution of two variables $x(t)$, $y(t)$ is said to be Gaussian if the probability density is given by

$$p(x, y) = \frac{1}{2\pi(\sigma_x{}^2\sigma_y{}^2 - \sigma_{xy}{}^4)^{\frac{1}{2}}} \exp\left[-\frac{\sigma_y{}^2 x^2 - 2\sigma_{xy}{}^2 xy + \sigma_x{}^2 y^2}{2(\sigma_x{}^2\sigma_y{}^2 - \sigma_{xy}{}^4)} \right] \quad (5)$$

where $\sigma_x{}^2$, $\sigma_y{}^2$ are the variances of $x(t)$, $y(t)$ and $\sigma_{xy}{}^2 = \langle x(t)\, y(t) \rangle$ is called the *covariance*.

When there are three variables the form of the probability density of a Gaussian distribution is somewhat more complicated, but it must be given here for use in subsequent analysis. For a three-dimensional Gaussian probability distribution, if x, y, z have zero mean value,

$$p(x, y, z) = \frac{1}{(2\pi)^{3/2}(\det M)^{\frac{1}{2}}} \exp\left[-\frac{1}{2\det M}\, (M_{xx}x^2 + M_{yy}y^2 + M_{zz}z^2 \right.$$

$$\left. + 2M_{yz}yz + 2M_{zx}zx + 2M_{xy}xy) \right], \quad (6)$$

where $\qquad \det M = \begin{vmatrix} \sigma_x{}^2 & \sigma_{xy}{}^2 & \sigma_{zx}{}^2 \\ \sigma_{xy}{}^2 & \sigma_y{}^2 & \sigma_{yz}{}^2 \\ \sigma_{zx}{}^2 & \sigma_{yz}{}^2 & \sigma_z{}^2 \end{vmatrix}$

and $M_{xx} = \sigma_y{}^2\sigma_z{}^2 - \sigma_{yz}{}^4$, $M_{yy} = \sigma_z{}^2\sigma_x{}^2 - \sigma_{zx}{}^4$, $M_{zz} = \sigma_x{}^2\sigma_y{}^2 - \sigma_{xy}{}^4$,

$$M_{yz} = \sigma_{xy}{}^2\sigma_{zx}{}^2 - \sigma_x{}^2\sigma_{yz}{}^2, \quad M_{zx} = \sigma_{yz}{}^2\sigma_{xy}{}^2 - \sigma_y{}^2\sigma_{zx}{}^2,$$

$$M_{xy} = \sigma_{zx}{}^2\sigma_{yz}{}^2 - \sigma_z{}^2\sigma_{xy}{}^2,$$

in which $\sigma_x{}^2$, $\sigma_{yz}{}^2$, etc., indicate $\langle x^2(t) \rangle$, $\langle y(t)\, z(t) \rangle$, etc.

The general expression for the n-dimensional Gaussian probability density may be found in the literature: see e.g. Bendat (reference 1, p. 118).

2.8 Correlations

The extent to which two random variables $x(t)$, $y(t)$ are correlated has some quantitative measure in the magnitude of the covariance $\sigma_{xy}{}^2 = \langle x(t)\, y(t) \rangle$. If $x(t)$ and $y(t)$ are completely independent $\sigma_{xy}{}^2 = 0$. If they are not independent $\sigma_{xy}{}^2$ will in general be other than zero and this will have an effect on the combined probability density.

We shall later find it necessary to extend this idea to cover the cross-correlations of signals measured at different times and to consider the quantity $\langle x(t)\,y(t+\tau)\rangle$: for a stationary random process this would be independent of t, and dependent only on τ. We shall also be interested in the quantity $R(\tau) = \langle x(t)\,x(t+\tau)\rangle$ which is called the *autocorrelation function*. The reasons for the importance of these quantities will become apparent later as the quantities themselves become familiar.

2.9 The Need for More Complete Description

We have seen that the distribution function $P(x)$ or the probability density $p(x)$ of a random signal $x(t)$ can give a good deal of information about $x(t)$. The signal can by its nature never be completely described, and a description in terms of probabilities is obviously far better than none at all. To know the probability distribution of a stress, so that we can know the probability of a given critical stress being exceeded at any time, obviously is a useful step towards solution of the design problem.

But we have not yet exhausted our capacity for description. A prescribed probability density only prescribes the proportion of time which a quantity spends in a certain range: we may know that the stress in a structural member will exceed a certain level for one minute during its life-time but unless we know whether this minute is made up of spells of ten seconds or of ten microseconds we shall not know much about its probable effect either in giving rise to vibration or to failure. We must therefore devise some means of describing the manner of the fluctuation of a quantity in addition to our means for describing its level distribution.

This can be done by using the autocorrelation function $R(\tau)$ mentioned in the previous paragraph. It is however more convenient for our present purpose to make use of a development of the normal processes of harmonic analysis; a description in terms of frequency content is also very useful in determining responses. In the next chapter, therefore, we shall consider how harmonic analysis can be adapted in this way.

CHAPTER III

HARMONIC ANALYSIS

3.1 Introduction

Harmonic analysis as it is usually understood is not applicable to random processes. But the basic methods and concepts of harmonic analysis can be developed in such a way as to make them applicable, and this having been done we have an additional way of describing a randomly varying quantity, and moreover all the advantages of harmonic analysis in the determination of response are available to us. The ideas of Fourier series, integrals, and transforms are in fact fundamental to our analysis of random processes and we must first establish the basic results concerning them. We shall assume as before that our stationary ergodic random process is sufficiently represented by a single typical randomly varying signal $x(t)$. We shall begin by considering the analysis of a periodic $x(t)$, and then of a non-periodic transient $x(t)$ before proceeding to the analysis of the random $x(t)$ in which we are really interested.

3.2 Fourier Series

If $x(t)$ is periodic, with period $T = 2\pi/\omega_1$, it can be expanded as a series of harmonically varying quantities in the form:

$$x(t) = a_0 + \sum_1^\infty (a_r \cos r\omega_1 t + b_r \sin r\omega_1 t) \tag{1}$$

where

$$
\left.
\begin{aligned}
a_0 &= \frac{1}{T} \int_{-T/2}^{T/2} x(t)\, dt, \\
a_r &= \frac{2}{T} \int_{-T/2}^{T/2} x(t) \cos r\omega_1 t\, dt, \\
b_r &= \frac{2}{T} \int_{-T/2}^{T/2} x(t) \sin r\omega_1 t\, dt.
\end{aligned}
\right\} \tag{2}
$$

This can be proved easily enough by expanding the right-hand sides of (2), substituting the expression (1) for $x(t)$. The terms of the series are sinusoids whose frequencies are multiples of the fundamental frequency ω_1, and the amplitudes of the various components can thus be plotted to give a discrete spectrum in which the spectral lines have spacing ω_1.

It is possible to express $\langle x^2(t) \rangle$, the mean-square value of $x(t)$, in terms of the coefficients a_r, b_r: squaring (1) and integrating over the period $T = 2\pi/\omega_1$ we have

$$\int_{-T/2}^{T/2} x^2(t)\, dt = a_0^2\, T + \sum_1^\infty \left(a_r^2\, \frac{T}{2} + b_r^2\, \frac{T}{2} \right),$$

all other product terms (such as $2a_r a_s \cos r\omega_1 t \cos s\omega_1 t$) vanishing on integration over the period. Thus

$$\langle x^2(t) \rangle = \frac{1}{T} \int_{-T/2}^{T/2} x^2(t)\, dt = a_0^2 + \tfrac{1}{2} \sum_1^\infty (a_r^2 + b_r^2). \qquad (3)$$

This is a form of Parseval's theorem.

A periodic function $x(t)$ can also be expressed as a series in complex form, giving

$$x(t) = \sum_{-\infty}^\infty c_r\, e^{ir\omega_1 t}, \qquad (4)$$

where

$$c_r = \frac{1}{T} \int_{-T/2}^{T/2} x(t)\, e^{-ir\omega_1 t}\, dt. \qquad (5)$$

This is most easily proved by using our previous results (2). Thus from (5) and (2),

$$\left. \begin{aligned} c_r &= \frac{1}{T} \int_{-T/2}^{T/2} x(t)(\cos r\omega_1 t - i \sin r\omega_1 t)dt = \tfrac{1}{2}(a_r - ib_r), \\ c_{-r} &= \frac{1}{T} \int_{-T/2}^{T/2} x(t)(\cos r\omega_1 t + i \sin r\omega_1 t)dt = \tfrac{1}{2}(a_r + ib_r), \\ \text{and} \quad c_0 &= \frac{1}{T} \int_{-T/2}^{T/2} x(t)\, dt = a_0. \end{aligned} \right\} \quad (9)$$

This gives $\quad x(t) = c_0 + \sum_1^\infty c_r\, e^{ir\omega_1 t} + \sum_1^\infty c_{-r}\, e^{-ir\omega_1 t}$ (from (4))

$$= a_0 + \sum_1^\infty \tfrac{1}{2}(a_r - ib_r)\,(\cos r\omega_1 t + i \sin r\omega_1 t)$$
$$+ \sum_1^\infty \tfrac{1}{2}(a_r + ib_r)\,(\cos r\omega_1 t - i \sin r\omega_1 t)$$
$$= a_0 + \sum_1^\infty [a_r \cos r\omega_1 t + b_r \sin r\omega_1 t], \text{ as before.}$$

Again the mean-square value of $x(t)$ can be expressed in terms of the coefficients: now

$$\langle x^2(t) \rangle = \sum_{-\infty}^\infty |c_r|^2. \tag{7}$$

This result can be proved by expanding the right-hand side and using (6):

$$\sum_{-\infty}^\infty |c_r|^2 = |c_0|^2 + \sum_1^\infty |c_r|^2 + \sum_1^\infty |c_{-r}|^2,$$
$$= a_0^2 + \sum_1^\infty \tfrac{1}{4}(a_r^2 + b_r^2) + \sum_1^\infty \tfrac{1}{4}(a_r^2 + b_r^2),$$
$$= a_0^2 + \tfrac{1}{2} \sum_1^\infty (a_r^2 + b_r^2),$$
$$= \langle x^2(t) \rangle, \text{ by (3).}$$

3.3 Fourier Integrals

A non-periodic function – a transient loading, for example – clearly can only be expressed as a Fourier series if we consider it to be periodic, with infinite period. When we do this our fundamental frequency is infinitesimal, so that the discrete spectrum closes up to give a continuous curve, and the series becomes an integral.

Let us assume that the fundamental frequency ω_1 is very small and denote it by $\Delta\omega$. Then we may write, combining 3.2(4) and 3.2(5),

$$x(t) = \sum_{-\infty}^\infty \frac{\Delta\omega}{2\pi} \int_{-T/2}^{T/2} x(t)\, e^{-ir\,\Delta\omega\, t}\, dt\; e^{ir\,\Delta\omega\, t}.$$

If we now let $\Delta\omega$ become the infinitesimal $d\omega$, the period T will tend to infinity: the summation must now include a continuous sequence of frequencies, so that the summation becomes an integral and $r\,\Delta\omega$ becomes simply ω. We have, therefore, when the period is infinite – where there is in fact no periodicity – the result

$$x(t) = \int_{-\infty}^{\infty} \left[\frac{d\omega}{2\pi} \int_{-\infty}^{\infty} x(t)\, e^{-i\omega t}\, dt\, e^{i\omega t} \right].$$

This we may conveniently write as two equations corresponding to 3.2(4) and 3.2(5): thus

$$x(t) = \frac{1}{2\pi} \int_{-\infty}^{\infty} A(i\omega)\, e^{i\omega t}\, d\omega, \tag{1}$$

$$\text{with } A(i\omega) = \int_{-\infty}^{\infty} x(t)\, e^{-i\omega t}\, dt. \tag{2}$$

Equations (1) and (2) give the *Fourier integral* expression for $x(t)$. The quantity $A(i\omega)$ defined by (2) is called the *Fourier transform* of $x(t)$; it is a function of ω – and in general complex – and it shows how $x(t)$ may be considered to be distributed over the frequency range. The response of a linear system due to a transient loading can, in principle, always be determined by expressing the loading in the form (1) and calculating and adding the separate responses corresponding to each infinitesimal strip $A(i\omega)d\omega$ of the Fourier transform spectrum, (although this is not always the best way to solve such a problem). The function $x(t)$ is said to be the *inverse transform* of $A(i\omega)$: the two quantities $x(t)$ and $A(i\omega)$ related by (1) and (2) are said to be a *Fourier transform pair*.

The near symmetry of (1) and (2) is very striking and is often made more so by dividing the coefficient $1/2\pi$ into two factors $1/\sqrt{(2\pi)}$ and giving one to each equation; the equations then differ only in the sign of the exponent. This device is, however, unnecessary if we work in terms of the actual frequency f instead of the circular frequency ω. Putting $\omega = 2\pi f$ in (1) and (2) we have

$$x(t) = \int_{-\infty}^{\infty} A(if)\, e^{i2\pi ft}\, df, \tag{3}$$

$$\text{with } A(if) = \int_{-\infty}^{\infty} x(t)\, e^{-i2\pi ft}\, dt. \tag{4}$$

As there are good practical reasons for working in terms of f we shall always use this form of the Fourier transform relationship.

It is possible to obtain a form of Parseval's theorem for this case also. We shall denote the complex conjugate of the Fourier transform $A(if)$ by writing $A^*(if)$: clearly, by (4), this is given by

$$A^*(if) = \int_{-\infty}^{\infty} x(t)\, e^{i2\pi ft}\, dt. \tag{5}$$

We know also that it is a property of complex conjugates that

$$A(if)\, A^*(if) = |A(if)|^2. \tag{6}$$

Thus

$$\int_{-\infty}^{\infty} x^2(t)\, dt = \int_{-\infty}^{\infty} x(t)\, x(t)\, dt$$

$$= \int_{-\infty}^{\infty} x(t) \left[\int_{-\infty}^{\infty} A(if)\, e^{i2\pi ft}\, df \right] dt$$

$$= \int_{-\infty}^{\infty} A(if) \left[\int_{-\infty}^{\infty} x(t)\, e^{i2\pi ft}\, dt \right] df,$$

changing the order of integration,

$$= \int_{-\infty}^{\infty} A(if)\, A^*(if)\, df, \quad \text{by (5)},$$

$$= \int_{-\infty}^{\infty} |A(if)|^2\, df, \tag{7}$$

by (6).

It is often convenient in practical applications to consider only positive frequencies: in such cases (7) can be rewritten in the form

$$\int_{-\infty}^{\infty} x^2(t)\, dt = 2 \int_{0}^{\infty} |A(if)|^2\, df \tag{8}$$

because $|A(if)|^2$ is an even function of f.

The result (8) will prove valuable in the next section.

3.4 Spectral Density

The results of the previous paragraphs are not as they stand applicable to random signals. A random signal is not periodic and so cannot well be expressed as a Fourier series. And examination of 3.3(4) shows that it cannot be expressed as a Fourier integral either: to have stationary properties a random signal must be assumed to continue over an infinite time, and in such a case neither the real nor the imaginary part of the Fourier transform converges to a steady value. Moreover we are not looking for a description only of a single function of time $x(t)$, which a Fourier integral would provide:

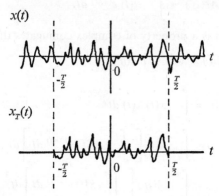

Fig. 3.4-1

we must have a description equally applicable to any other member function of the random process $\{x(t)\}$ which might instead have been generated by the physical system under consideration. From our results, however, it is possible to develop a new quantity, the *spectral density*, which has no convergence difficulties and which is applicable to a whole class of similarly generated functions.

Consider a member function $x(t)$ of a stationary random process. As the signal may be assumed to have commenced at $t = -\infty$ and must be presumed to continue until $t = \infty$, we cannot define its Fourier transform, $A(if)$. There is no difficulty, however, in determining the Fourier transform $A_T(if)$ of a signal $x_T(t)$ which we define to be identical with $x(t)$ over the interval $-\dfrac{T}{2} < t < \dfrac{T}{2}$ and to be zero at all other times, as shown in Fig. 3.4-1.

We can therefore use equation 3.3(8) to express the mean-square value of $x_T(t)$ in terms of $A_T(if)$, as follows:

$$\langle x_T{}^2(t) \rangle = \frac{1}{T} \int_{-T/2}^{T/2} x_T{}^2(t)\, dt$$

$$= \frac{1}{T} \int_{-\infty}^{\infty} x_T{}^2(t)\, dt$$

$$= \frac{2}{T} \int_{0}^{\infty} |A_T(if)|^2\, df. \tag{1}$$

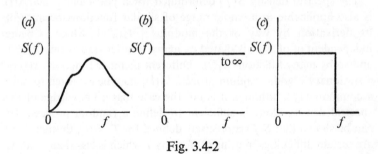

Fig. 3.4-2

If we now let $T \to \infty$, we obtain an expression for the mean-square value of $x(t)$, i.e.

$$\langle x^2(t) \rangle = \int_0^\infty \lim_{T \to \infty} \left[\frac{2}{T} \, | \, A_T(if) \, |^2 \right] df$$

$$= \int_0^\infty S(f) \, df, \tag{2}$$

where we have written

$$S(f) = \lim_{T \to \infty} \left[\frac{2}{T} \, | \, A_T(if) \, |^2 \right]. \tag{3}$$

The quantity $S(f)$ is called the *spectral density* of the function $x(t)$ and it will figure largely in our subsequent discussions. It is formally defined by (3), but its properties are best appreciated by considering (2). From (2) it can be seen that the form of $S(f)$ indicates the manner of the distribution of the harmonic content of the signal over the frequency range from zero frequency to infinite frequency (as in Fig. 3.4-2(a)): the amount of $\langle x^2(t) \rangle$ associated with a narrow band of frequency Δf is simply $S(f) \, \Delta f$. (This can be considered as the mean-square value of the signal passed by a narrow-band filter of band-width Δf). Its dimensions will depend on those of $x(t)$: if, for example, $x(t)$ is acceleration then $S(f)$ might well be expressed as g^2/cps.

Spectral density is more precisely – though not very aptly for our purposes – described as 'power spectral density', the nomenclature deriving from its use in electrical problems, where a randomly varying current $x(t)$ through unit resistance gives a mean power consumption of $\langle x^2(t) \rangle$.

The spectral density $S(f)$ determined for a particular signal $x(t)$ is also applicable to a whole range of similar functions because of its derivation by way of the modulus $|A_T(if)|$, which – being independent of phase – is shared by many Fourier transforms $A_T(if)$, and so by many functions $x_T(t)$. Different member functions $x(t)$ of a stationary ergodic random process $\{x(t)\}$ may be expected to have a common $S(f)$, although it is not the case that a knowledge of the spectral density alone is sufficient to define a random process. (It can be shown that $S(f)$ is precisely defined for $T = \infty$, though there are certain difficulties in using (3) for any T which is less than infinity. We shall consider this last point in greater detail later.) The harmonic content of all member functions of a stationary random process $\{x(t)\}$ can therefore be described by a single spectrum in which $S(f)$ is plotted against the frequency f as in Fig. 3.4-2(a), the shape of the spectrum depending on the way in which the process is generated.

In general the spectral density is a function of frequency but there are cases in which it is approximately constant over a wide frequency range, and it is therefore natural to consider the implications of a random process whose spectrum is uniform over the full frequency range from zero to infinity as in Fig. 3.4-2(b): such a spectrum is then said to be 'white' by a rather imperfect analogy with white light, and such a signal is often referred to as *white noise*. A white spectrum in this sense could not occur in practice because, as inspection of (2) will show, a finite spectral density would then imply an infinite mean-square value. But results obtained by assuming a white spectrum are often meaningful; we might, for example, satisfactorily determine the response of a system to a loading uniform only over a limited range by assuming a white noise excitation, knowing that the system would not respond appreciably to the higher frequencies. In all work on random processes it is possible to consider a white spectrum to terminate at some frequency beyond the range of interest as in Fig. 3.4-2(c) and $S(f)$ can be explicitly assumed to have such a form, with a definite cut-off frequency, if this refinement is thought to be desirable.

Measurement of $S(f)$ is in principle easily accomplished on the basis of (2) by means of a narrow-band filter, provided that the signal $x(t)$ can conveniently be transformed into electrical form. There are certain difficulties intrinsic to the use of a signal not of infinite length which we must consider later. For the present however it may be convenient to visualise $S(f)$ as being measured in this way.

3.5 Spectral Density and Probability Distribution

In general a knowledge of the spectral density of a random process does not enable us to determine its probability density or distribution function; if the spectral density is known it is easy to determine the mean-square value, but this tells us little about the distribution.

If however a process is known to be Gaussian, the whole distribution is defined by the mean-square value, or variance σ^2, by means of the relation 2.5(1):

$$p(x) = \frac{1}{\sigma\sqrt{(2\pi)}} e^{-x^2/2\sigma^2}, \tag{1}$$

it being assumed that the mean value is zero. As

$$\sigma^2 = \langle x^2(t) \rangle = \int_0^\infty S(f)\, df \tag{2}$$

a knowledge of the spectral density is sufficient to give the probability density, and hence the distribution function if it is required. If the mean value is not zero, equation (1) can be modified accordingly provided that the mean value is known.

It is thus very fortunate that so many physical random processes have probability distributions which are, or are approximately, Gaussian.

3.6 Autocorrelation Function

We must now introduce another important quantity, which although apparently very different from spectral density is nevertheless very closely related to it, as we shall see: this is the *autocorrelation function*. For a randomly varying quantity $x(t)$ the autocorrelation function $R(\tau)$ is defined by

$$R(\tau) = \langle x(t)\, x(t+\tau) \rangle. \tag{1}$$

Thus we take the value of a quantity $x(t)$ at any time t and multiply it by the value when a further time τ has elapsed; we do this for all values of t and then take the mean value of all such products. If we assume – as we normally shall – that we are dealing with a member function $x(t)$ of a stationary ergodic random process, $R(\tau)$ will also be the autocorrelation function of any other member function of the

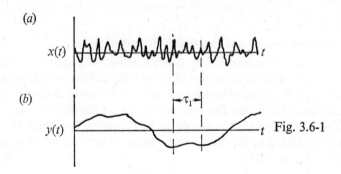

Fig. 3.6-1

process. Under these circumstances, provided that the averaging is carried out over a sufficient length of record, $R(\tau)$ will be independent of t and dependent only on τ.

Let us consider first the case where the mean value of $x(t)$ is zero. Then we can see that for very large values of τ the value of $R(\tau)$ must be zero: if two values $x(t)$ and $x(t+\tau)$ are separated by a very long interval τ they will be quite unrelated to each other, so that some products $x(t)\,x(t+\tau)$ will be positive and some negative, the values being scattered symmetrically on either side of the value zero. The mean value of all these products will be zero, so that

$$R(\infty) = 0.$$

For the other extreme case, $\tau = 0$, the definition gives

$$R(0) = \langle x^2(t) \rangle \qquad (2)$$

which is simply the mean-square value of $x(t)$; as all the products are squares the mean value must be positive. If τ is other than zero, but very small, the value of each $x(t+\tau)$ cannot have changed appreciably from its corresponding $x(t)$, so that most products will be positive, and $R(\tau)$ will be positive though rather less than $R(0)$. For increasing values of τ the factors of each product will become less and less related to each other, until $R(\tau)$ falls effectively to zero, possibly with some slight fluctuation about the zero value before the factors become effectively unrelated.

The value of τ at which $R(\tau)$ falls effectively to zero gives an index of the suddenness of the fluctuations of $x(t)$. Reference to Fig. 3.6-1 shows that for two different randomly varying quantities $x(t)$ and

$y(t)$ a given interval τ_1 can give rise to factors $x(t)$ and $x(t+\tau_1)$ which have little relationship to each other if – as in Fig. 3.6-1(a) – the fluctuations of $x(t)$ occur rapidly in relation to τ_1, or to closely connected factors $y(t)$ and $y(t+\tau_1)$ if – as in Fig. 3.6-1(b) – the fluctuations of $y(t)$ are slow in relation to τ_1. Thus the form of the autocorrelation function of a signal is seen to be dependent on its frequency content, and so on the spectral density.

If the mean value of a randomly varying quantity $x(t)$ is other than zero, equations (1) and (2) still apply, but it is no longer the case that $R(\infty) = 0$ as a little consideration will show. Suppose that the mean value of $x(t)$ is known: then we may write

$$x(t) = \langle x(t) \rangle + \xi(t),$$

where $\xi(t)$ represents the fluctuating part of $x(t)$, and has mean value zero. Then representing the autocorrelation functions of $x(t)$, $\xi(t)$, by $R_x(\tau)$, $R_\xi(\tau)$, we have

$$\begin{aligned} R_x(\tau) &= \langle x(t)\, x(t+\tau) \rangle \\ &= \langle [\langle x(t) \rangle + \xi(t)][\langle x(t+\tau) \rangle + \xi(t+\tau)] \rangle \\ &= \langle \langle x(t) \rangle \langle x(t+\tau) \rangle + \langle x(t) \rangle\, \xi(t+\tau) \\ &\quad + \xi(t)\langle x(t+\tau) \rangle + \xi(t)\, \xi(t+\tau) \rangle. \end{aligned}$$

But for a stationary ergodic random process, $\langle x(t+\tau) \rangle = \langle x(t) \rangle$ and $\langle \xi(t+\tau) \rangle = \langle \xi(t) \rangle = 0$, so that

$$\begin{aligned} R_x(\tau) &= \langle x(t) \rangle^2 + \langle \xi(t)\, \xi(t+\tau) \rangle \\ &= \langle x(t) \rangle^2 + R_\xi(\tau). \end{aligned} \tag{3}$$

It is perhaps worth noting that for $\tau = 0$ this is in agreement with 2.4(2).

The relationship between autocorrelation function $R(\tau)$ and spectral density $S(f)$ is much closer than the mere qualitative correspondence which we have described above: there is a direct analytical relationship between the two, and if one is known the other may be deduced.

Let us obtain an expression for the Fourier transform of $R(\tau)$. To do this we shall again find it convenient to make use of the function $x_T(t)$ which coincides with $x(t)$ over the range $-T/2 < t < T/2$ and is zero at all other times. We can then define

$$R(\tau) = \lim_{T \to \infty} R_T(\tau) = \lim_{T \to \infty} \langle x_T(t)\, x_T(t+\tau) \rangle,$$

where $R_T(\tau)$ is the autocorrelation function of $x_T(t)$, the mean being taken over the interval T. We have

$$\int_{-\infty}^{\infty} R_T(\tau)\, e^{-i2\pi f\tau}\, d\tau = \int_{-\infty}^{\infty} \left[\frac{1}{T}\int_{-\infty}^{\infty} x_T(t)x_T(t+\tau)dt\right] e^{-i2\pi f\tau}\, d\tau$$

$$= \frac{1}{T}\int_{-\infty}^{\infty}\left[\int_{-\infty}^{\infty} x_T(t)\, x_T(t+\tau)\, e^{-i2\pi f\tau}\, dt\right] d\tau$$

$$= \frac{1}{T}\int_{-\infty}^{\infty}\left[\int_{-\infty}^{\infty} x_T(t)\, x_T(t+\tau)\, e^{i2\pi ft}\, e^{-i2\pi f(t+\tau)}\, dt\right] d\tau$$

$$= \frac{1}{T}\int_{-\infty}^{\infty}\left[\int_{-\infty}^{\infty} x_T(t)\, x_T(s)\, e^{i2\pi ft}\, e^{-i2\pi fs}\, dt\right] ds$$

$$= \frac{1}{T}\int_{-\infty}^{\infty} x_T(t)\, e^{i2\pi ft}\, dt \int_{-\infty}^{\infty} x_T(s)\, e^{-i2\pi fs}\, ds$$

$$= \frac{1}{T}\, A_T{}^*(if)\, A_T(if),$$

where $A_T{}^*(if)$ indicates the complex conjugate of $A_T(if)$,

$$= \frac{1}{T}\, |\, A_T(if)\,|^2.$$

But we know that $\lim\limits_{T\to\infty} \dfrac{2}{T}\, |\, A_T(if)\,|^2 = S(f),$ by 3.4(3), and so, letting $T \to \infty$, so that $R_T(\tau)$ becomes $R(\tau)$, we find that

$$S(f) = \int_{-\infty}^{\infty} 2R(\tau)\, e^{-i2\pi f\tau}\, d\tau. \tag{4}$$

There is thus a Fourier transform relationship between spectral density $S(f)$ and autocorrelation function $R(\tau)$, $S(f)$ being the Fourier transform of $2R(\tau)$.

It follows of course from (4) that

$$R(\tau) = \int_{-\infty}^{\infty} \tfrac{1}{2}S(f)\, e^{i2\pi f\tau}\, df; \tag{5}$$

i.e. $R(\tau)$ is the inverse transform of $\frac{1}{2}S(f)$. Equations (4) and (5) are often referred to as the Wiener-Khinchin relations.

The factor 2 arising in equations (4) and (5) is a consequence of our definition of $S(f)$ to give a spectrum extending only over fre-

quencies between 0 and ∞, as seems desirable for engineering purposes, and not over all those between $-\infty$ and $+\infty$ which would
be more convenient mathematically. It may be noted, however, that
although equations 3.3(8) and 3.4(2) make no use of negative frequencies, equation 3.4(3) does define $S(f)$ satisfactorily for negative
frequencies if it should prove desirable to make use of them: there
is thus no difficulty in using (5).

The fact that autocorrelation function and spectral density form a
Fourier transform pair is very useful to us. Although in random
vibration work the spectral density is usually the more convenient
to measure, the autocorrelation function is often more convenient to
use in analysis. The relationship existing between them makes it
possible to work in terms of whichever proves most convenient for a
particular operation. It is also the case, because of 3.5(2), that for a
Gaussian random process a knowledge of $R(\tau)$ is sufficient to determine the whole probability distribution.

The relationship between $R(\tau)$ and $S(f)$ given by (4) and (5) can
also be expressed using integrals taken between zero and infinity,
i.e. for positive values only of time and frequency. The need to
consider negative frequencies can thus be avoided.
Thus

$$R(\tau) = \int_{-\infty}^{\infty} \tfrac{1}{2}S(f)\, e^{i2\pi f\tau}\, df$$

$$= \int_{0}^{\infty} \tfrac{1}{2}S(f)\, e^{i2\pi f\tau}\, df + \int_{-\infty}^{0} \tfrac{1}{2}S(f)\, e^{i2\pi f\tau}\, df$$

$$= \int_{0}^{\infty} \tfrac{1}{2}S(f)\, e^{i2\pi f\tau}\, df + \int_{0}^{-\infty} \tfrac{1}{2}S(-f)\, e^{-i2\pi(-f)\tau}\, d(-f),$$

using the fact that $S(f)$ is even, which may
be inferred from 3.3(4) and 3.4(3),

$$= \int_{0}^{\infty} \tfrac{1}{2}S(f)\, e^{i2\pi f\tau}\, df + \int_{0}^{\infty} \tfrac{1}{2}S(g)\, e^{-i2\pi g\tau}\, dg$$

$$= \int_{0}^{\infty} S(f)\cos 2\pi f\tau\, df. \qquad (6)$$

Conversely, $S(f) = 4 \int_{0}^{\infty} R(\tau)\cos 2\pi f\tau\, d\tau.$ \qquad (7)

We can use these relationships to show that the autocorrelation

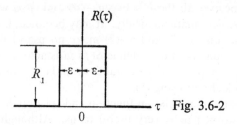

Fig. 3.6-2

function of a white noise signal – that is, of a randomly varying quantity having a spectral density independent of frequency – is a Dirac δ-function. (The Dirac δ-function, $\delta(\tau)$, is defined such that $\delta(\tau) = 0$ for all values of τ other than zero, but such that

$$\int_{0-}^{0+} \delta(\tau)\, d\tau = 1.)$$

This is best demonstrated by starting from the autocorrelation function.

Suppose that the autocorrelation function $R(\tau)$ of a certain random process is as shown in Fig. 3.6-2, rectangular in form, having $R(\tau) = R_1$ for $-\varepsilon < \tau < \varepsilon$ and being zero for all other values of τ.

Then from (7)

$$S(f) = 4 \int_0^\varepsilon R_1 \cos 2\pi f\tau \, d\tau$$

$$= \frac{4R_1}{2\pi f} \sin 2\pi f\varepsilon.$$

If ε is sufficiently small this reduces to $4R_1\varepsilon$, which is twice the area under the rectangle. In the limiting case therefore where $R(\tau) = A\delta(\tau)$, with area A under the rectangle, the spectral density is given by

$$S(f) = 2A:$$

the spectrum is in fact white.

Conversely if the spectral density $S(f) = S_1$, then the autocorrelation function $R(\tau) = \frac{1}{2}S_1\delta(\tau)$.

This result is acceptable on physical grounds; white noise contains harmonic components of infinitesimal period, so that a quantity can change with great suddenness, and correlation over any but infinitesimal values of τ cannot be expected. We know also that for white noise the mean-square value is infinite: as the autocorrelation function is equal to the mean-square value for $\tau = 0$ it must follow that $R(\tau)$ is also infinite for $\tau = 0$.

Reference 14 has a particularly good account of the autocorrelation function.

3.7 Some Properties of the Autocorrelation Function

There are certain properties of the autocorrelation function and its derivatives which are useful in analysis.

Clearly $R(\tau)$ is an even function of τ:

$$\begin{aligned}R(\tau) &= \langle x(t)\,x(t+\tau)\rangle, \\ &= \langle x(t-\tau)\,x(t)\rangle, \text{ (for a stationary random process)} \\ &= R(-\tau).\end{aligned} \tag{1}$$

We are sometimes concerned with the values of the differentials of $R(\tau)$, particularly at $\tau = 0$. The differential can be obtained by differentiating the factor containing τ; thus, using a prime to indicate differentiation with respect to the contents of a bracket,

$$R'(\tau) = \langle x(t)\,x'(t+\tau)\rangle.$$

But equally, putting $\qquad R(\tau) = \langle x(t-\tau)\,x(t)\rangle,$

we have $R'(\tau) = \langle -x'(t-\tau)\,x(t)\rangle.$

Putting $\tau = 0$ we have therefore $\langle x(t)\,x'(t)\rangle = -\langle x'(t)\,x(t)\rangle$, which can only be true if both are zero. Thus

$$R'(0) = 0. \tag{2}$$

Similarly $R''(\tau) = \dfrac{\partial}{\partial \tau}\langle x(t)\,x'(t+\tau)\rangle$

$$= \frac{\partial}{\partial \tau}\langle x(t-\tau)\,x'(t)\rangle$$

$$= -\langle x'(t-\tau)\,x'(t)\rangle,$$

so that, putting $\tau = 0$, we have

$$R''(0) = -\langle x'^{2}(t)\rangle. \tag{3}$$

We can also show in the same way that

$$R'''(0) = 0, \tag{4}$$

$$R''''(0) = \langle x''^{2}(t)\rangle, \text{ etc.} \tag{5}$$

The mean-square value of any derivative of $x(t)$ can thus be determined if $R(\tau)$ is known. Clearly the converse is not true.

These mean-square values can also be expressed directly in terms of the spectral density $S(f)$. Using the relationship 3.6(6) we have

$$R(\tau) = \int_0^\infty S(f) \cos 2\pi f\tau \, df$$

and so

$$R'(\tau) = -2\pi \int_0^\infty f\, S(f) \sin 2\pi f\tau \, df, \tag{6}$$

$$R''(\tau) = -4\pi^2 \int_0^\infty f^2 \, S(f) \cos 2\pi f\tau \, df, \text{ etc.}$$

Putting $\tau = 0$ in (6) we obtain

$$\langle x^2(t) \rangle = R(0) \quad = \int_0^\infty S(f) \, df,$$

$$\langle x'^2(t) \rangle = -R''(0) = 4\pi^2 \int_0^\infty f^2 \, S(f) \, df, \tag{7}$$

$$\langle x''^2(t) \rangle = R''''(0) \quad = 16\pi^4 \int_0^\infty f^4 \, S(f) \, df, \text{ etc.}$$

3.8 Combinations of Random Processes

It is sometimes necessary to determine the spectral density or autocorrelation function of a quantity which is a combination of a number of different randomly varying quantities, for each of which the spectral density or autocorrelation function is already known. We may be interested for example in the relative motion of two points rather than in their two separate displacements, or in the motion of a point due to two separate excitations acting together. It is therefore necessary that we be able to determine the spectral density and autocorrelation function of a sum in terms of those of its constituents.

Consider a randomly varying quantity $z(t)$ made up of two quantities $x(t)$ and $y(t)$, so that $z(t) = x(t) + y(t)$: let us try to express the spectral density $S_z(f)$ and autocorrelation function $R_z(\tau)$ of the quantity $z(t)$ in terms of the separate spectral densities $S_x(f)$, $S_y(f)$ and the separate autocorrelation functions $R_x(\tau)$, $R_y(\tau)$ of its constituents $x(t)$ and $y(t)$.

The autocorrelation function of the combined signal $R_z(\tau)$ can be expanded as follows:

$$
\begin{aligned}
R_z(\tau) &= \langle z(t)\, z(t+\tau) \rangle \\
&= \langle [x(t)+y(t)][x(t+\tau)+y(t+\tau)] \rangle \\
&= \langle x(t)\, x(t+\tau)+x(t)\, y(t+\tau)+y(t)\, x(t+\tau)+y(t)\, y(t+\tau) \rangle \\
&= \langle x(t)\, x(t+\tau) \rangle + \langle x(t)\, y(t+\tau) \rangle + \langle y(t)\, x(t+\tau) \rangle \\
&\qquad\qquad\qquad\qquad\qquad\qquad\quad + \langle y(t)\, y(t+\tau) \rangle.
\end{aligned} \tag{1}
$$

The first and last terms of (1) are simply the autocorrelation functions $R_x(\tau)$ and $R_y(\tau)$ with which we are already familiar. The second and third terms are *cross-correlation functions* (briefly mentioned in 2.8) and they are denoted by $R_{xy}(\tau)$, $R_{yx}(\tau)$, giving

$$
\left.
\begin{aligned}
R_{xy}(\tau) &= \langle x(t)\, y(t+\tau) \rangle \\
R_{yx}(\tau) &= \langle y(t)\, x(t+\tau) \rangle.
\end{aligned}
\right\} \tag{2}
$$

We see therefore that it is not possible to determine the combined autocorrelation function if we know only the autocorrelation functions of the constituents: we must know the cross-correlation functions also. These will be zero if it happens that $x(t)$ and $y(t)$ are completely unrelated: if however they are in any way related – as for example if $x(t)$ and $y(t)$ are the displacements of different points of a body due to the same loading – $R_{xy}(\tau)$ and $R_{yx}(\tau)$ will not be zero, and they must be taken into account in determining $R_z(\tau)$. The autocorrelation function of the sum $z(t)$ of two quantities $x(t)$ and $y(t)$ is therefore given by the expression

$$
R_z(\tau) = R_x(\tau)+R_{xy}(\tau)+R_{yx}(\tau)+R_y(\tau). \tag{3}
$$

Where the combined signal $z(t)$ consists of more than two quantities, so that

$$
z(t) = x_1(t)+x_2(t)+ \ldots +x_n(t),
$$

we can show that the autocorrelation function $R_z(\tau)$ is given by

$$
R_z(\tau) = \sum_{r=1}^{n} \sum_{s=1}^{n} R_{x_r x_s}(\tau), \tag{4}
$$

where $R_{x_1 x_1}(\tau)$, for example, is to be interpreted as $R_{x_1}(\tau)$.

Knowing the relationship between autocorrelation function and spectral density, we may infer that the spectral density of the combined quantity cannot be derived if only the two separate spectral densities are known.

For $z(t) = x(t)+y(t)$ we shall have, in fact,

$$S_z(f) = \int_{-\infty}^{\infty} 2R_z(\tau)\, e^{-i2\pi f\tau}\, d\tau$$

$$= 2 \int_{-\infty}^{\infty} [R_x(\tau)+R_{xy}(\tau)+R_{yx}(\tau)+R_y(\tau)]\, e^{-i2\pi f\tau}\, d\tau$$

$$= S_x(f)+S_{xy}(f)+S_{yx}(f)+S_y(f), \tag{5}$$

where we have had to introduce two more new quantities, the *cross spectral densities*, defined by

$$\left.\begin{array}{l} S_{xy}(f) = 2 \displaystyle\int_{-\infty}^{\infty} R_{xy}(\tau)\, e^{-i2\pi f\tau}\, d\tau, \\[2mm] S_{yx}(f) = 2 \displaystyle\int_{-\infty}^{\infty} R_{yx}(\tau)\, e^{-i2\pi f\tau}\, d\tau. \end{array}\right\} \tag{6}$$

These relations are closely analogous to those connecting spectral density and autocorrelation function given in 3.6(4) and 3.6(5).

Our defining the cross spectral densities in (5) by relating them to the corresponding cross-correlation functions is convenient and explicit, but they can also be defined in a manner closely analogous to our original definition of spectral density in 3.4(3), as we shall now show.

Suppose that $x_T(t)$, $y_T(t)$ coincide exactly with $x(t)$, $y(t)$ in the range $-T/2 < t < T/2$ and are zero at all other times: let us write

$$R_{x_T y_T}(\tau) = \langle x_T(t)\, y_T(t+\tau)\rangle.$$

Then

$$\int_{-\infty}^{\infty} R_{x_T y_T}(\tau)\, e^{-i2\pi f\tau}\, d\tau = \int_{-\infty}^{\infty} \langle x_T(t)\, y_T(t+\tau)\rangle\, e^{-i2\pi f\tau}\, d\tau$$

$$= \int_{-\infty}^{\infty} \frac{1}{T} \int_{-\infty}^{\infty} x_T(t)\, y_T(t+\tau)\, dt\, e^{-i2\pi f\tau}\, d\tau$$

$$= \frac{1}{T} \int_{-\infty}^{\infty} \left[\int_{-\infty}^{\infty} x_T(t)\, y_T(t+\tau)\, e^{-i2\pi f\tau}\, dt \right] d\tau$$

$$= \frac{1}{T} \int_{-\infty}^{\infty} \left[\int_{-\infty}^{\infty} x_T(t)\, e^{i2\pi ft}\, y_T(t+\tau)\, e^{-i2\pi f(t+\tau)}\, dt \right] d\tau$$

$$= \frac{1}{T} \int_{-\infty}^{\infty} x_T(t)\, e^{i2\pi ft}\, dt \int_{-\infty}^{\infty} y_T(t+\tau)\, e^{-i2\pi f(t+\tau)}\, d(t+\tau)$$

$$= \frac{1}{T} \int_{-\infty}^{\infty} x_T(t)\, e^{i2\pi ft}\, dt \int_{-\infty}^{\infty} y_T(t)\, e^{-i2\pi ft}\, dt,$$

$$= \frac{1}{T} A_T{}^*(f)\, B_T(f), \tag{7}$$

writing $A_T(f)$, $B_T(f)$ as the Fourier transforms of $x_T(t)$, $y_T(t)$.

So

$$S_{xy}(f) = 2 \int_{-\infty}^{\infty} R_{xy}(\tau)\, e^{-i2\pi f\tau}\, d\tau, \qquad \text{by (6)},$$

$$= \lim_{T \to \infty} \left[\frac{2}{T} A_T{}^*(f)\, B_T(f) \right], \tag{8}$$

by (7).

We may note that this reduces to 3.4(3) if $x(t) = y(t)$.

These cross-correlation parameters are likely to be important in problems of response where, as often happens, a body is excited by a number of forces acting at different points, or where we are interested in the relative motions of different points.

3.9 Properties of Cross-Correlation Parameters

Some special properties of cross-correlation functions and cross spectral densities become apparent when we consider their definitions. We shall see that apart from their more obvious differences they differ from the autocorrelation function and direct spectral density in certain important ways. Consider first

$$R_{xy}(\tau) = \langle x(t)\, y(t+\tau) \rangle: \tag{1}$$

if a pair of randomly varying loadings are stationary in the sense we have been considering, the quantity $R_{xy}(\tau)$ will remain independent of time for any given τ. Thus

$$R_{xy}(\tau) = \langle x(t-\tau)\, y(t) \rangle,$$
$$= R_{yx}(-\tau) \tag{2}$$

by definition. But we cannot, on the other hand, obtain any relationship between $R_{xy}(\tau)$ and $R_{xy}(-\tau)$, which are as independent as any other pair $R_{xy}(\tau_1)$ and $R_{xy}(\tau_2)$. Hence $R_{xy}(\tau)$ and $R_{yx}(\tau)$ are in general unrelated.

The cross spectral density is defined by

$$S_{xy}(f) = 2 \int_{-\infty}^{\infty} R_{xy}(\tau)\, e^{-i2\pi f\tau}\, d\tau. \tag{3}$$

This we may write as

$$S_{xy}(f) = 2 \left[\int_{0}^{\infty} R_{xy}(\tau)\, e^{-i2\pi f\tau}\, d\tau - \int_{-\infty}^{0} R_{yx}(-\tau)\, e^{i2\pi f(-\tau)}\, d(-\tau) \right]$$

$$= 2 \left[\int_{0}^{\infty} R_{xy}(\tau)\, e^{-i2\pi f\tau}\, d\tau + \int_{0}^{\infty} R_{yx}(\tau)\, e^{i2\pi f\tau}\, d\tau \right]. \tag{4}$$

If $R_{xy}(\tau)$ and $R_{yx}(\tau)$ were equal, (4) would indicate that $S_{xy}(f)$ was real. As they are usually not, we see that $S_{xy}(f)$ is, in general, a complex quantity. (It has been considered preferable to use the symbol $S_{xy}(f)$ rather than $S_{xy}(if)$ although this might seem rather more consistent).

Using (3) and substituting $R_{yx}(-\tau)$ for $R_{xy}(\tau)$, we have

$$S_{xy}(f) = 2 \int_{-\infty}^{\infty} R_{yx}(-\tau)\, e^{i2\pi f(-\tau)}\, d\tau$$

$$= -2 \int_{-\tau=\infty}^{-\tau=-\infty} R_{yx}(-\tau)\, e^{i2\pi f(-\tau)}\, d(-\tau)$$

$$= 2 \int_{-\infty}^{\infty} R_{yx}(\tau)\, e^{i2\pi f\tau}\, d\tau.$$

But by definition $S_{yx}(f) = 2 \displaystyle\int_{-\infty}^{\infty} R_{yx}(\tau)\, e^{-i2\pi f\tau}\, d\tau,$

and so we see that $S_{xy}(f)$ and $S_{yx}(f)$ are complex conjugates.

3.10 Summary of Principal Results

It will be an advantage if before proceeding further we collect together for easy reference those results and definitions of Chapters II and III which will be most frequently used in the analysis of subsequent chapters.

The *distribution function* $P(x)$ of a quantity $x(t)$ or a process $\langle x(t) \rangle$

is defined as the probability that, at any instant, $x(t)$ shall be not greater than x, or in symbols

$$P(x) = \text{Pr}[x(t) \leq x].$$ 2.3(1)

This probability distribution for any instant of time also describes the way in which the values of $x(t)$ are distributed with respect to time over any sufficiently long record.

The *probability density* $p(x)$ is defined by

$$p(x) = \frac{dP(x)}{dx},$$ 2.2(2)

or $$P(x) = \int_{-\infty}^{x} p(z) \, dz.$$ 2.2(3)

A signal $x(t)$ with zero mean value is said to have a *Gaussian distribution* if

$$p(x) = \frac{1}{\sigma \sqrt{(2\pi)}} e^{-x^2/2\sigma^2},$$ 2.5(1)

where the quantity σ^2 is called the *variance* and is simply the mean-square value of the signal, i.e.

$$\sigma^2 = \langle x^2(t) \rangle.$$

A function $x(t)$ and its *Fourier transform* $A(if)$ are related by

$$x(t) = \int_{-\infty}^{\infty} A(if) \, e^{i2\pi ft} \, df,$$ 3.3(3)

$$A(if) = \int_{-\infty}^{\infty} x(t) \, e^{-i2\pi ft} \, dt.$$ 3.3(4)

The *spectral density* $S(f)$ of a quantity $x(t)$ is defined, by way of these relations, such that

$$\langle x^2(t) \rangle = \int_{0}^{\infty} S(f) \, df.$$ 3.4(2)

Here $S(f)$ is in fact given by

$$S(f) = \lim_{T \to \infty} \left[\frac{2}{T} \, | \, A_T(if) \, |^2 \right],$$ 3.4(3)

where $A_T(if)$ is the Fourier transform of a function $x_T(t)$ defined to coincide with $x(t)$ over the interval $-T/2 < t < T/2$ and to be zero elsewhere. A spectrum is said to be 'white' if $S(f)$ is constant at all frequencies.

The *autocorrelation function* $R(\tau)$ of a quantity $x(t)$ is defined by

$$R(\tau) = \langle x(t)\, x(t+\tau) \rangle. \qquad 3.6(1)$$

There exists between spectral density and autocorrelation function a Fourier transform relationship such that

$$S(f) = \int_{-\infty}^{\infty} 2R(\tau)\, e^{-i2\pi f\tau}\, d\tau, \qquad 3.6(4)$$

$$R(\tau) = \int_{-\infty}^{\infty} \tfrac{1}{2}S(f)\, e^{i2\pi f\tau}\, df. \qquad 3.6(5)$$

These relations can also be expressed in the form

$$S(f) = \int_{0}^{\infty} 4R(\tau)\cos 2\pi f\tau\, d\tau, \qquad 3.6(7)$$

$$R(\tau) = \int_{0}^{\infty} S(f)\cos 2\pi f\tau\, df. \qquad 3.6(6)$$

It follows from 3.6(4) and 3.4(2) that for a process with a Gaussian distribution a knowledge of either spectral density or autocorrelation function is sufficient to define σ^2 and so, by 2.5(1), the whole probability distribution.

Two signals $x(t)$ and $y(t)$ have also a *cross spectral density* $S_{xy}(f)$ and a *cross-correlation function* $R_{xy}(\tau)$ defined such that

$$R_{xy}(\tau) = \langle x(t)\, y(t+\tau) \rangle, \qquad 3.8(2)$$

$$S_{xy}(f) = \int_{-\infty}^{\infty} 2R_{xy}(\tau)\, e^{-i2\pi f\tau}\, d\tau. \qquad 3.8(6)$$

CHAPTER IV

RESPONSE TO A SINGLE RANDOM LOADING

4.1 Introduction

The concepts of the two previous chapters enable us to describe a single random process as well as we are ever likely to be able to describe it. When we define the probability density and the spectral density of a particular randomly varying force record, for example, we are describing it as completely as we can without making our description inapplicable to other member functions of the same random process. So in determining the response of a system to random excitation – in determining the stress, say, due to a randomly varying applied force – we shall obviously not expect to know it in any greater detail than that in which we can describe the excitation. Our aim in determining the response of a system to random loading is therefore to be able to specify the spectral density (or autocorrelation function) and the probability density (or distribution function) of the response, when the corresponding properties of the excitation are known.

As we are concerned here with random vibration, which is the motion of a system due to randomly varying applied forces, we shall concentrate on developing analysis which will enable us to describe this motion. But although we shall consider specifically the displacements arising due to a randomly varying force, similar results can easily be obtained if some related quantity such as acceleration or stress is to be found, or indeed if the relationship between response and excitation for any other linear system is to be investigated. We shall confine our attention to linear systems: in this chapter we shall consider only the response to single excitations.

Before treating the response of a system to a randomly varying force, however, it is necessary that we consider certain aspects of the response of systems to *known* forces: we must consider in particular the response of systems to sinusoidal loadings and to impulsive loadings. Our analysis of these problems will lead directly to analysis giving the response to random loading in general terms. We shall find that in order to determine the response of a particular system to random loading we need to have available results giving the response of the system to sinusoidal excitation. Such results can be obtained either experimentally or by the use of well established analytical techniques of the theory of vibrations, including particularly normal mode analysis. Many readers will be familiar with these methods, but for those who are not a brief account has been provided in the Appendix.

4.2 Response to Periodic and Transient Loadings

Let us consider first the response of a simple spring-mass system as shown in Fig. 4.2-1 to a sinusoidally varying force $P(t) = P_0 \cos \omega t$. We shall assume that the damping is viscous.

The equation of motion may be written as

$$m\ddot{x} + c\dot{x} + kx = P_0 \, e^{i\omega t}. \tag{1}$$

Here the right-hand side is written $P_0 \, e^{i\omega t}$, which is equal to $P_0 (\cos \omega t + i \sin \omega t)$, on the understanding that only the real part of the solution is to be taken: all terms giving the response to the superfluous term $P_0 \, i \sin \omega t$ will be clearly labelled by the presence of the imaginary quantity i.

The particular integral of (1), which gives the steady-state solution, is clearly of the form $x = x_0 \, e^{i\omega t}$, where the quantity x_0 may of course be complex. Thus substituting in (1), we obtain

$$(-\omega^2 m + i\omega c + k)x_0 = P_0,$$

giving

$$x_0 = \frac{P_0}{k - m\omega^2 + i\omega c}.$$

This is conveniently written as

$$x_0 = \alpha(i\omega) \, P_0, \tag{2}$$

where

$$\alpha(i\omega) = \frac{1}{k - m\omega^2 + i\omega c}. \tag{3}$$

The required particular integral of (1) is thus

$$x = \frac{P_0}{k - m\omega^2 + i\omega c} \, e^{i\omega t}$$

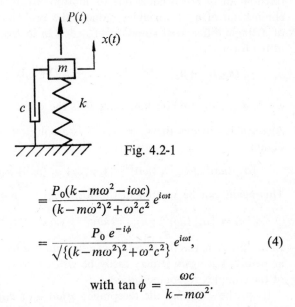

Fig. 4.2-1

$$= \frac{P_0(k - m\omega^2 - i\omega c)}{(k - m\omega^2)^2 + \omega^2 c^2} e^{i\omega t}$$

$$= \frac{P_0 e^{-i\phi}}{\sqrt{\{(k - m\omega^2)^2 + \omega^2 c^2\}}} e^{i\omega t}, \qquad (4)$$

$$\text{with } \tan \phi = \frac{\omega c}{k - m\omega^2}.$$

The response to the actual force, $P_0 \cos \omega t$, being the real part of (4), is therefore

$$\frac{P_0}{\sqrt{\{(k - m\omega^2)^2 + \omega^2 c^2\}}} \cos (\omega t - \phi). \qquad (5)$$

It should be noted that the form of (5) can be written down immediately by inspection of the quantity $\alpha(i\omega)$ defined by (3), indicating as it does both magnitude and phase relative to the exciting force. This quantity, defined as in (2) to give the response of the system to a complex force of unit modulus and proportional to $e^{i\omega t}$, is called the *receptance* of the system.

It is often desirable to work in terms of actual frequency f, rather than the circular frequency. In such cases the symbol $\alpha(i\omega)$ for receptance may be replaced by $\alpha(if)$, which in the present case is defined by

$$\alpha(if) = \frac{1}{k - 4\pi^2 m f^2 + i2\pi f c}. \qquad (6)$$

In the more general problem of a system having n degrees of freedom there are n equations of motion involving n unknowns: elimination of $n-1$ variables reduces the problem to the solution of a single differential equation of order $2n$ in a single variable x, in the form

$$(a_{2n}D^{2n}+a_{2n-1}D^{2n-1}+ \ldots +a_1 D+a_0)x = P_0 e^{i\omega t}, \qquad (7)$$

where a_{2n}, etc., are constants and D is the differential operator $\dfrac{d}{dt}$. Again it is obvious that $x = x_0\, e^{i\omega t}$ is a solution: substituting, we obtain

$$[a_{2n} (i\omega)^{2n}+a_{2n-1} (i\omega)^{2n-1}+ \ldots +a_1 (i\omega)+a_0]\, x_0 = P_0.$$

This again can be written in the form $x_0 = \alpha(i\omega)\, P_0$, where now

$$\alpha(i\omega) = [a_{2n} (i\omega)^{2n}+a_{2n-1} (i\omega)^{2n-1}+ \ldots +a_1 (i\omega)+a_0]^{-1}.$$

In this problem too the response can be obtained by the same process as before, but again it may easily be written down after inspection of the complex receptance $\alpha(i\omega)$.

It will be seen that the receptance $\alpha(i\omega)$ – or $\alpha(if)$ – determined analytically or by experiment, provides virtually complete description of the response of any linear system to sinusoidal excitation. The response to any non-sinusoidal periodic force can be determined by superposition, expressing the excitation as a Fourier series and adding the responses to the separate components with a proper regard to phase. We shall also find that the receptance $\alpha(if)$ is particularly valuable in determining response to random excitation. (Further information about receptances is to be found in reference 2.)

The response to a transient force can be determined from the receptance by using the Fourier integral technique, but it is usually more convenient to make use of the Duhamel integral, which expresses the response in terms of the response to unit impulse. This method we must now introduce.

An impulsive loading can be expressed mathematically as

$$P(t) = I\, \delta(t)$$

where I is the magnitude of the impulse, and $\delta(t)$ is the Dirac δ-function (defined such that $\delta(t) = 0$ for $t \neq 0$, but with

$$\int_{0-}^{0+} \delta(t)\, dt = 1).$$

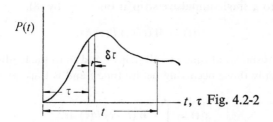

$P(t)$

$\delta\tau$

τ

t

t, τ Fig. 4.2-2

The response to such a loading may be expressed as

$$x(t) = W(t)I \qquad (8)$$

where the function $W(t)$, which gives the response to a unit impulse, must be determined for the particular system being considered.

It is best here to consider a specific example. Our simple spring-mass system subjected to an impulse I at $t = 0$ and starting from rest has an equation of motion

$$m\ddot{x} + c\dot{x} + kx = I\,\delta(t) \qquad (9)$$

and its solution may be shown to be (for $t > 0$)

$$x = \frac{I}{m\omega_1} e^{-\Delta t} \sin \omega_1 t, \qquad (10)$$

where $\omega_1^2 = \dfrac{k}{m} - \left(\dfrac{c}{2m}\right)^2$, and $\Delta = c/2m$. (This solution applies equally to the equation of motion $m\ddot{x} + c\dot{x} + kx = 0$ with initial conditions $x = 0$, $\dot{x} = I/m$, but the formulation of (9) provides a better basis for the use of Duhamel's integral later.) For this case therefore we have

$$W(t) = \frac{1}{m\omega_1} e^{-\Delta t} \sin \omega_1 t. \qquad (11)$$

Let us now use this result to find the response to a loading $P(t)$ which is not impulsive but continuous with time. The area under the $P(t)$, t curve (Fig. 4.2-2) can be divided into a large number of impulsive loadings, the impulse due to each being represented by a strip of area $P(\tau)\,\delta\tau$, where τ is the local value of t. The response at time t to a single impulsive strip at time τ is, by (8),

$$x(t) = W(t-\tau)\,P(\tau)\,\delta\tau.$$

The total response at time t to all strips – and so to the loading $P(t)$ – includes only those occurring before time t and is thus given by the integral

$$x(t) = \int_{-\infty}^{t} W(t-\tau)\,P(\tau)\,d\tau. \tag{12}$$

This is known as Duhamel's integral, or the *convolution* integral.

Duhamel's integral can be expressed in another form by changing the variable: if we write $\tau' = t - \tau$, and express (12) in terms of the new variable τ' we obtain

$$x(t) = \int_{\infty}^{0} W(\tau')\,P(t-\tau')\,(-d\tau')$$

$$= \int_{0}^{\infty} W(\tau)\,P(t-\tau)\,d\tau. \tag{13}$$

There is an interesting relationship between $\alpha(if)$ and $W(\tau)$ as we shall find by using (13) to investigate the response to sinusoidal excitation. The response of a system to a force $P(t) = P_0\,e^{i2\pi f t}$ is given by

$$x(t) = \int_{0}^{\infty} W(\tau)\,P_0\,e^{i2\pi f(t-\tau)}\,d\tau$$

$$= P_0\,e^{i2\pi f t} \int_{0}^{\infty} W(\tau)\,e^{-i2\pi f \tau}\,d\tau. \tag{14}$$

But we know that for this case

$$x(t) = \alpha(if)\,P_0\,e^{i2\pi f t}:$$

thus $$\alpha(if) = \int_{0}^{\infty} W(\tau)\,e^{-i2\pi f \tau}\,d\tau \tag{15}$$

which is the Fourier transform of $W(\tau)$, if $W(\tau)$ is assumed to be zero for $\tau < 0$.

These results will be needed when we consider the response of a system to random loading in the next section.

4.3 Response to Random Loading

In developing analysis which will give the response to random excitation we shall consider the displacement response of a mechanical system to a randomly varying force. We shall denote the force by $P(t)$, and shall suppose it to have autocorrelation function $R_P(\tau)$ and spectral density $S_P(f)$: the resulting displacement will be denoted by $x(t)$ and its autocorrelation function and spectral density by $R_x(\tau)$ and $S_x(f)$. We shall assume that there is a single applied force and that we are concerned only with the displacement of a single point, and also that the directions of force and displacement are fixed, so that the parameters of the system $\alpha(if)$ and $W(t)$ are explicit. It is our object, if it be possible, to determine $R_x(\tau)$ in terms of $R_P(\tau)$, and $S_x(f)$ in terms of $S_P(f)$. We shall also be interested in any connection between the two probability distributions.

(a) Autocorrelation Functions.

We shall treat first the problem of predicting the autocorrelation function of the response: to do this we must expand the quantity

$$R_x(\tau) = \langle x(t)\, x(t+\tau)\rangle.$$

We have from 4.2(13)

$$\left.\begin{aligned}
x(t) &= \int_0^\infty W(\tau_1)\, P(t-\tau_1)\, d\tau_1, \\
x(t+\tau) &= \int_0^\infty W(\tau_2)\, P(t+\tau-\tau_2)\, d\tau_2.
\end{aligned}\right\} \tag{1}$$

Distinction between the three variables τ_1, τ_2, τ appearing in (1) will be found to be essential. To evaluate $R_x(\tau)$ we must integrate the product over all combinations of τ_1 and τ_2, and we require a further separate variable τ as the argument of $R_x(\tau)$.

So $\quad R_x(\tau) = \langle x(t)\, x(t+\tau)\rangle$

$$= \int_0^\infty W(\tau_1) \int_0^\infty W(\tau_2)\langle P(t-\tau_1)\, P(t+\tau-\tau_2)\rangle d\tau_2\, d\tau_1$$

$$= \int_0^\infty W(\tau_1) \int_0^\infty W(\tau_2)\langle P(t)\, P(t+\tau_1-\tau_2+\tau)\rangle d\tau_2\, d\tau_1,$$

a change in origin of t making no difference to the meaned quantity if the process is stationary,

$$= \int_0^\infty W(\tau_1) \int_0^\infty W(\tau_2)\, R_P(\tau_1 - \tau_2 + \tau)\, d\tau_2\, d\tau_1. \qquad (2)$$

From which it will be seen that although $R_x(\tau)$ can be determined from $R_P(\tau)$, its calculation is not a simple process. The result (2) will however prove very useful in finding the relationship between the spectral densities.

(b) Spectral Densities.

The relationship between the spectral densities can be obtained most easily from (2) by making use of the Fourier transform relationship between autocorrelation function and spectral density.
We have from 3.6(4)

$$S_x(f) = 2 \int_{-\infty}^\infty R_x(\tau)\, e^{-i2\pi f \tau}\, d\tau$$

$$= 2 \int_{-\infty}^\infty \left[\int_0^\infty W(\tau_1) \int_0^\infty W(\tau_2)\, R_P(\tau_1 - \tau_2 + \tau)\, d\tau_2\, d\tau_1 \right] e^{-i2\pi f \tau}\, d\tau$$

$$= 2 \int_0^\infty W(\tau_1) \int_0^\infty W(\tau_2) \left[\int_{-\infty}^\infty R_P(\tau_1 - \tau_2 + \tau)\, e^{-i2\pi f \tau}\, d\tau \right] d\tau_2\, d\tau_1$$

$$= 2 \int_0^\infty W(\tau_1)\, e^{i2\pi f \tau_1} \int_0^\infty W(\tau_2)\, e^{-i2\pi f \tau_2} \int_{-\infty}^\infty R_P(\tau_1 - \tau_2 + \tau)$$
$$e^{-i2\pi f(\tau_1 - \tau_2 + \tau)}\, d(\tau_1 - \tau_2 + \tau)\, d\tau_2\, d\tau_1$$

$$= 2 \int_0^\infty W(\tau_1)\, e^{i2\pi f \tau_1}\, d\tau_1 \int_0^\infty W(\tau_2)\, e^{-i2\pi f \tau_2}\, d\tau_2$$
$$\times \int_{-\infty}^\infty R_P(\tau_1 - \tau_2 + \tau)\, e^{-i2\pi f(\tau_1 - \tau_2 + \tau)}\, d(\tau_1 - \tau_2 + \tau).$$

The separate factors of this expression are identifiable (using 4.2(15) and 3.6(4)) as $\alpha^*(if)$, $\alpha(if)$ and $\tfrac{1}{2}S_P(f)$, so that

$$S_x(f) = 2\alpha^*(if)\,\alpha(if)\,\tfrac{1}{2}S_P(f),$$

or finally,

$$S_x(f) = |\alpha(if)|^2\, S_P(f). \qquad (3)$$

Equation (3) gives a particularly simple relationship between the spectral densities of excitation and response. The spectral density of the displacement at any frequency is equal to the spectral density of the exciting force at that frequency, multiplied by the square of the modulus of the receptance at that frequency. The receptance of a system can always be determined in terms of frequency either analytically or by measuring the response experimentally over the frequency range, and as we are concerned only with the modulus $|\alpha(if)|$ our experimental determination need not concern itself with phase: a straight-forward response curve is sufficient.

Fig. 4.3-1 shows some experimental results which illustrate this relationship. The actual quantities $P(t)$ and $x(t)$ are shown in (a). The spectrum $S_P(f)$ of the applied force $P(t)$ is shown in (b); the response curve obtained by discrete frequency excitation is shown in (c); the spectral density $S_x(f)$ of the resulting displacement $x(t)$ is shown in (d). At low frequencies the response spectral density $S_x(f)$ is small because $|\alpha(if)|$ is small (and $|\alpha(if)|^2$ is smaller); the $S_x(f)$ curve shows the two peaks of $|\alpha(if)|^2$, indicating a high content of these two frequencies – that at the lower frequency being more prominent because of the form of $S_P(f)$. The relatively large high-frequency content of $P(t)$ can be seen in (a), as can the predominance of the two peak frequencies in $x(t)$.

The curves shown in Fig. 4.3-1 were in fact obtained using an analogue computer circuit to simulate a system having two degrees of freedom and fairly heavy damping, as the peaks of response curves of actual vibrating systems are usually far too pronounced to provide a suitable illustration. In practice the spectral density $S_x(f)$ of response in random vibration does usually give a sharply peaked curve, because the frequency-response curve obtained by plotting $|\alpha(if)|$ against f is itself sharply peaked for most systems susceptible to vibration. The spectral density $S_P(f)$ of a randomly varying force on the other hand usually varies only slowly with frequency, so that a white noise loading may offer an adequate representation over a limited frequency range. Obviously the spectral density plot of the response to a white noise loading has exactly the form of the $|\alpha(if)|^2$ response curve because $S_P(f)$ is then independent of frequency.

The plotting of spectra on logarithmic paper – the use in effect of logarithmic coordinates – is a common practice, and it does possess some real advantages. There is, for example, no difficulty in plotting sharply-peaked spectra or receptances; very different responses occurring over a wide frequency range can be accommodated; and the multiplication of $S_P(f)$ and $|\alpha(if)|^2$ to obtain $S_x(f)$ is very easily carried out by simple addition. But spectra plotted in this way can

(a)

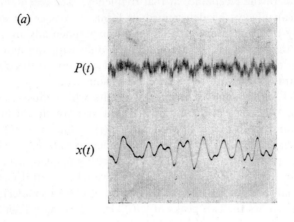

(b)

(c)

(d)

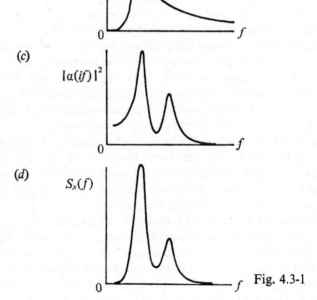

Fig. 4.3-1

easily be misinterpreted by those more used to linear plots, and some care is needed until familiarity has been achieved.

Once the spectral density of a quantity has been found there is no difficulty in principle in obtaining other related quantities such as the autocorrelation function or the mean-square value. It is therefore not difficult, for example, to relate the mean-square value of the applied randomly varying force to the mean-square value of the resulting displacement.

(c) Probability Distributions.

A knowledge of the spectral density of a quantity is not in itself sufficient to define its probability distribution, and there is in general no simple relationship connecting, for example, the probability density of the excitation with that of the response. But if we also know that the excitation is Gaussian it can be shown that the response is Gaussian also, and in this case the probability densities of excitation and response can be obtained immediately from their spectral densities.

The response to an exciting force $P(t)$ is given by equation 4.2(13)

i.e.
$$x(t) = \int_0^\infty W(\tau)\, P(t-\tau)d\tau. \tag{4}$$

If $P(t)$ is Gaussian, then $P(t-\tau)$ must be Gaussian also, and the integral of (4) can be considered as the limiting case of a linear sum of Gaussian variables, of the form $\sum a_r X_r$. As it is known (see reference 1, p. 111) that such a sum does have a Gaussian distribution we can deduce that in the limiting case also the distribution of $x(t)$ is Gaussian.

In this case, therefore,

$$p_x(x) = \frac{1}{\sigma_x \sqrt{(2\pi)}}\, e^{-x^2/2\sigma_x^2}, \tag{5}$$

where
$$\sigma_x^2 = \langle x^2(t) \rangle = \int_0^\infty S_x(f)\, df.$$

The mean-square value of the output $\langle x^2(t) \rangle$ is of course itself a quantity of some practical interest, but there are often easier ways of measuring it directly.

4.4 Limitations

Before we demonstrate the application of the results which we have obtained to particular systems, it should be noted that in obtaining them our attention has been deliberately confined to the case where there is a single exciting force. The problem of the response to two or more randomly varying forces is more complex and will be treated in Chapter V. Meanwhile the reader should note this limitation and realise that the careless use of superposition in random vibration problems is likely to be hazardous. Even where there is only a single applied force it should be remembered that the spectral density gives the spectrum of the *mean-square*; thus doubling a quantity $x(t)$ implies quadrupling its spectral density $S(f)$, or its autocorrelation function $R(\tau)$.

4.5 Response of Spring-Mass System to Random Excitation

Let us now apply the result 4.3(3) to determine the response of a simple spring-mass system, as shown in Fig. 4.5-1, to an exciting force $P(t)$ having spectral density $S_P(f)$: we shall suppose the damping to be viscous.

To find the spectral density $S_x(f)$ of the motion $x(t)$ we must first find the complex receptance $\alpha(if)$ of the system; this was shown in Section 4.2 to be given by

$$\alpha(if) = \frac{1}{k - 4\pi^2 m f^2 + i2\pi f c}. \tag{1}$$

It follows, therefore, that

$$|\alpha(if)|^2 = \frac{1}{(k - 4\pi^2 m f^2)^2 + 4\pi^2 f^2 c^2}. \tag{2}$$

So the spectral density of the displacement is by 4.3(3) simply

$$S_x(f) = \frac{S_P(f)}{(k - 4\pi^2 m f^2)^2 + 4\pi^2 f^2 c^2}. \tag{3}$$

The mean-square value of the displacement can be found from (3) by making use of the relationship

$$\langle x^2(t) \rangle = \int_0^\infty S_x(f)\, df. \tag{4}$$

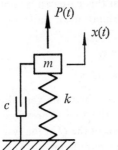

Fig. 4.5-1

Clearly similar results to (3) could be obtained in the same way for the spectral densities of velocity and acceleration. If it is known that $x(t)$ is Gaussian, (4) together with 4.3(5) defines the whole probability distribution.

If the excitation is white, with uniform spectral density S_P over the relevant frequency range, the spectral density plot of the displacement is identical in form to the $|\alpha(if)|^2$ curve. In this case the mean-square value is easily obtained by the use of (4): integration of (3) using residue theory gives

$$\langle x^2(t) \rangle = S_P \int_0^\infty \frac{df}{(k-4\pi^2 mf^2)^2 + 4\pi^2 f^2 c^2}$$

$$= \frac{S_P}{4ck}. \tag{5}$$

If we had considered instead a system with hysteretic damping, the equation of motion 4.2(1) would have been replaced by

$$m\ddot{x} + k(1+i\eta)\,x = P_0\,e^{i\omega t}, \tag{6}$$

where $\eta k x$ gives the magnitude of the damping force acting on m at any time, which is still 180° out of phase with velocity. The receptance is then given by

$$\alpha(if) = \frac{1}{k - 4\pi^2 mf^2 + i\eta k}, \tag{7}$$

so using 4.3(3) the spectral density of the response is given by

$$S_x(f) = \frac{S_P(f)}{(k - 4\pi^2 mf^2)^2 + \eta^2 k^2}. \tag{8}$$

The mean-square response in this case can be obtained as before by means of (4): for a white excitation of uniform spectral density S_P a similar integration gives

$$\langle x^2(t) \rangle = \frac{S_P}{4\eta k \sqrt{(km)}}. \tag{9}$$

Equation (9) appears at first sight to be very different from (5): if damping is small, however, the two expressions become identical when each is expressed in terms of the Q of the system (see Appendix). Substituting for the damping parameter in (5) and (9), using $Q = \sqrt{(km)}/c$ for viscous damping and $Q = 1/\eta$ for hysteretic damping, we obtain in both cases

$$\langle x^2(t) \rangle = \frac{S_P Q}{4k \sqrt{(km)}}. \tag{10}$$

The assumption of a white excitation here is reasonable if the system is lightly damped, because only that part of the $S_P(f)$ curve close to the natural frequency of the system can have any appreciable effect on the result. The spectral density of an exciting force is likely to be uniform over the small range of frequencies corresponding to the high portion of the response curve. The ineffectiveness of the greater part of the $S_P(f)$ spectrum is emphasised if we compare the mean-square magnitude of the random loading necessary to give a certain mean-square displacement with that of the harmonically varying force, suitably tuned, which gives the same mean-square displacement.

Suppose for example that the randomly varying force $P(t)$ is such that its spectral density $S_P(f)$ is constant up to a frequency f_c and zero above this. Then its mean-square value, $P^{(r)}_{ms}$ say, with the suffix (r) meaning random, is given by

$$P^{(r)}_{ms} = \int_0^{f_c} S_P(f) \, df = S_P f_c:$$

the mean-square displacement is given nearly enough by (10), assuming that f_c is well above the resonance frequency of the system, f_n. With harmonic excitation at the resonance frequency, the mean-square displacement is simply $Q^2 P^{(h)}_{ms}/k^2$, where $P^{(h)}_{ms}$ denotes the mean-square value of the *harmonic* loading. In order that the two mean-square displacements should be equal therefore, the forces must be such that

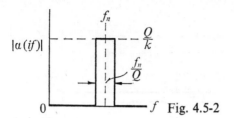

Fig. 4.5-2

$$\frac{Q^2 P_{ms}^{(h)}}{k^2} = \frac{S_P Q}{4k\sqrt{(km)}} = \frac{Q P_{ms}^{(r)}}{4k\sqrt{(km)}f_c},$$

giving

$$\frac{P_{ms}^{(h)}}{P_{ms}^{(r)}} = \frac{1}{4Q f_c} \sqrt{\frac{k}{m}} = \frac{\pi f_n}{2Q f_c}. \tag{11}$$

The ratio (11) is likely to be very small, as Q is large for most mechanical systems, and f_c is certainly larger than f_n.

It is sometimes convenient to obtain a rough approximation for the mean-square response to random loading by replacing the actual frequency-response curve by a simplified version having constant receptance over a narrow range of frequencies and nothing outside it, as shown in Fig. 4.5-2.

With this assumed frequency-response characteristic and white excitation we have

$$\langle x^2(t) \rangle = \int_0^\infty S_P(f) \, | \, \alpha(if) \, |^2 \, df$$

$$= S_P \left(\frac{Q}{k} \right)^2 \frac{f_n}{Q},$$

$$= \frac{S_P Q f_n}{k^2} = \frac{S_P Q}{2\pi k \sqrt{(km)}}, \tag{12}$$

which is at least of the same order as (10).

4.6 Response of Beam to Single Loading

We have considered in general terms the response of a linear system to a single random loading, and have shown that the spectral

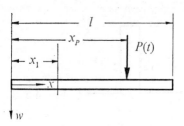

Fig. 4.6-1

density of the response can always be deduced from that of the excitation once the complex receptance $\alpha(if)$ of the system is known over the relevant frequency range. The receptance can always be obtained experimentally by measuring amplitude and phase with discrete-frequency excitation if the system already exists (and the measurement of phase can be dispensed with as the receptance is only to be used in the form $|\alpha(if)|$): if this is not the case an analytical approach is necessary, and we have already demonstrated the effectiveness of this on a single-degree-of-freedom system in Section 4.5.

We must now consider the extension of the analysis necessary to determine the response to random loading of more general systems. We shall consider first the response of a beam to random loading, partly because this problem is relevant to structural analysis and partly because although it is relatively simple the treatment shows the essential features of more complicated problems, with which in practice we are likely to be concerned. The general problem of the response to a single loading will be considered in Section 4.7.

Consider a beam of length l as shown in Fig. 4.6-1, with a transverse point load $P(t)$ acting at $x = x_P$: let us consider in particular the transverse displacement $w(x_1, t)$ at $x = x_1$.

To obtain the response to random $P(t)$ we must first obtain the relevant receptance $\alpha_{1P}(if)$, which defines the response at $x = x_1$ due to harmonic excitation of unit amplitude at x_P. To do this, therefore, we determine the response when $P(t) = P_0 e^{i\omega t}$.

We must first set up the equations of motion of the system, and Lagrange's Equations provide a convenient means for doing this. The displacement at any point, $w(x, t)$, may be expressed in terms of the normal modes of the beam as

$$w(x, t) = \sum_r w_r(x)\, \xi_r(t), \tag{1}$$

where $w_r(x)$ represents the rth normal mode of the beam and the $\xi_r(t)$ are consequently normal coordinates.

For a beam the kinetic energy at any time is given by

$$T = \tfrac{1}{2} \int_0^l \dot{w}^2(x, t) \, m \, dx \qquad (2)$$

where m is the mass per unit length (which is not necessarily uniform), and the integration is taken over the whole length of the beam. We may substitute from (1) to obtain

$$T = \tfrac{1}{2} \int_0^l \left[\sum_r w_r(x) \, \dot{\xi}_r(t) \right]^2 m \, dx,$$

and because normal coordinates are such that no $\dot{\xi}_r \, \dot{\xi}_s$ terms appear in the energy expression this becomes

$$T = \tfrac{1}{2} \int_0^l \left[\sum_r w_r^2(x) \, \dot{\xi}_r^2(t) \right] m \, dx$$

$$= \sum_r \left[\tfrac{1}{2} \int_0^l w_r^2(x) \, m \, dx \, \dot{\xi}_r^2(t) \right]$$

$$= \sum_r \tfrac{1}{2} M_r \, \dot{\xi}_r^2(t), \qquad (3)$$

where $M_r \left(= \int_0^l w_r^2(x) \, m \, dx \right)$ is the rth generalised mass.

We can also derive expressions for potential energy in the same way, but if we assume that the natural frequencies are likely to be known – and if we know the modes this will presumably be so – we can avoid doing this by using our knowledge of vibrations to predict the remaining term of the left-hand sides of the equations of motion directly: this must be such as to give, for each normal mode, the correct results in free vibration, that is

$$\ddot{\xi}_r + \omega_r^2 \, \xi_r = 0.$$

Damping can also be included, either by adding a further term proportional to $\dot{\xi}_r$, or, if we are considering sinusoidal motion, by including an imaginary part in the stiffness term. (It is assumed that the damping is small, and that there is no coupling between the modes due to damping). We shall use the latter alternative on the grounds that hysteretic damping gives a good approximation to the behaviour of an actual system. The exciting force is represented by generalised forces Ξ_r on the right-hand side of each equation.

The equation of motion in the rth normal mode is then

$$M_r \ddot{\xi}_r + M_r \omega_r{}^2 (1 + i\eta_r)\, \xi_r = \Xi_r.$$

The generalised force Ξ_r corresponding to ξ_r is obtained by considering the work done, δW, in a virtual displacement $\delta w(x)$. Thus for $P(t) = P_0\, e^{i\omega t}$,

$$\delta W = P_0\, e^{i\omega t}\, \delta w(x_P)$$
$$= P_0\, e^{i\omega t} \sum_r w_r(x_P)\, \delta\xi_r.$$

As Ξ_r must be such that $\delta W = \sum_r \Xi_r\, \delta\xi_r$, we see that

$$\Xi_r = w_r(x_P)\, P_0\, e^{i\omega t}.$$

The equations of motion may be written, therefore, as

$$M_r \ddot{\xi}_r + \omega_r{}^2(1 + i\eta_r)\, M_r \xi_r = w_r(x_P)\, P_0\, e^{i\omega t}, \tag{4}$$
$$(r = 1, 2, \ldots).$$

Solving (4) in the usual way we obtain

$$\xi_r = \frac{w_r(x_P)\, P_0\, e^{i\omega t}}{M_r(\omega_r{}^2 - \omega^2 + i\eta_r \omega_r{}^2)},$$

and thus, using (1),

$$w(x_1, t) = P_0\, e^{i\omega t} \sum_r \left[\frac{w_r(x_1)\, w_r(x_P)}{M_r} \times \frac{1}{\omega_r{}^2 - \omega^2 + i\eta_r \omega_r{}^2} \right].$$

Thus $w(x_1, t)$ is proportional to $e^{i\omega t}$; letting $w(x_1, t) = w_0(x_1)\, e^{i\omega t}$ we have

$$\alpha_{1P}(i\omega) = \frac{w_0(x_1)}{P_0} = \sum_r \left[\frac{w_r(x_1)\, w_r(x_P)}{M_r} \times \frac{1}{\omega_r{}^2 - \omega^2 + i\eta_r \omega_r{}^2} \right]$$

$$= \sum_r \left[\frac{w_r(x_1)\, w_r(x_P)}{M_r} \times \frac{\omega_r{}^2 - \omega^2 - i\eta_r \omega_r{}^2}{(\omega_r{}^2 - \omega^2)^2 + \eta_r{}^2 \omega_r{}^4} \right]. \tag{5}$$

We shall usually require the receptance to be expressed in terms of frequency $f\,(= \omega/2\pi)$; writing also $f_r = \omega_r/2\pi$ we obtain:

$$\alpha_{1P}(if) = \sum_r \mu_r(X_r - i\, Y_r), \tag{6}$$

$$\text{with } \mu_r = \frac{w_r(x_1)\, w_r(x_P)}{M_r},$$

$$X_r = \frac{f_r^2 - f^2}{4\pi^2[(f_r^2 - f^2)^2 + \eta_r^2 f_r^4]},$$

$$\text{and } Y_r = \frac{\eta_r f_r^2}{4\pi^2[(f_r^2 - f^2)^2 + \eta_r^2 f_r^4]}. \tag{6a}$$

This is the required receptance.

When there is random excitation $P(t)$, the spectral density $S_1(f)$ of the motion of x_1 is related to the spectral density $S_P(f)$ of $P(t)$, at any frequency, by

$$S_1(f) = |\alpha_{1P}(if)|^2\, S_P(f), \tag{7}$$

so we must now determine $|\alpha_{1P}(if)|^2$. From (6) we have

$$|\alpha_{1P}(if)|^2 = \left(\sum_r \mu_r X_r\right)^2 + \left(\sum_r \mu_r Y_r\right)^2. \tag{8}$$

The presence of product terms such as $\mu_r \mu_s\, X_r X_s$ when the summations are squared, prevents any further simplification.

Further simplification of the expression giving $|\alpha(if)|^2$ does become possible under certain circumstances in which approximation is permissible. If the damping of the system is small, the peaks of (8) will be pronounced, and provided that the natural frequencies are well separated, the expression (8) – and so the response – at any near-resonance frequency will be dominated by a single term of the summation. It follows that the product terms mentioned above will, at such frequencies, be small relative to one single $(X_r^2 + Y_r^2)$ term. Away from a resonance this will not be so, but in these regions some inaccuracy can be permitted because, as the magnitudes are so much smaller, such frequencies play little part in random vibration. Omitting the product terms, therefore, we obtain

$$|\alpha_{1P}(if)|^2 = \sum_r \mu_r^2 (X_r^2 + Y_r^2)$$

$$= \sum_r \frac{\mu_r^2}{16\pi^4[(f_r^2 - f^2)^2 + \eta_r^2 f_r^4]}. \tag{9}$$

If indeed only a single term is important near any one peak, this quantity need not be written as a series at all: we have then, nearly enough

$$|\alpha_{1P}(if)|^2 = \frac{\mu_r^2}{16\pi^4[(f_r^2-f^2)^2+\eta_r^2f_r^4]},$$ (10)

for f close to f_r $(r = 1, 2, 3 \ldots)$.

(This means that the value of r is to be taken which corresponds to the natural frequency f_r closest to the particular f. Thus, for example, we could use $r = 2$ for all frequencies in the range

$$\frac{f_1+f_2}{2} < f < \frac{f_2+f_3}{2}, \text{ etc.})$$

Whether we consider the response in the form of (8) or (10), it is possible to consider the response to depend on two factors: the μ_r, which depend on the positioning of loading and measurement points with respect to the normal modes, and the magnitudes of X_r, Y_r at the particular frequency. If, for any r, $w_r(x_1)$ or $w_r(x_P)$ is zero – that is if the loading or measuring device is situated at a node of any normal mode – then the μ_r for that r is zero, and there is no response in that mode. For an f close to any f_r, the corresponding mode will be greatly emphasised.

In this case therefore the spectral density $S_1(f)$ of the response will have the form given by (10) modified to some extent by the form of the spectral density $S_P(f)$ of the excitation.

4.7 General Response to Single Loading

In the previous section we considered the response of a beam. This analysis can be extended very easily to any other case in which the displacement of all points takes place in a single direction. By the use of vectors it can also be extended to the general case of the response of a three-dimensional system: this case we shall now consider.

Consider then the motions of a body of any shape. The position of any point in the body can be described by the position vector $\mathbf{p}$ relative to some origin. The displacement of a point originally at $\mathbf{p}$ after time t can be represented by a displacement vector $\mathbf{u}(\mathbf{p}, t)$: this can be expressed in terms of normal modes as

$$\mathbf{u}(\mathbf{p}, t) = \sum_r \mathbf{u}_r(\mathbf{p})\, \xi_r(t),$$ (1)

where the $\mathbf{u}_r(\mathbf{p})$ are the normal modes and the ξ_r the corresponding normal coordinates. The normal modes are now three-dimensional.

The body may be assumed to be excited by a randomly varying force $P(t)$ acting at a point p_P.

We must first investigate the response of the system to a loading $P = P_0 \, e^{i\omega t}$ acting at p_P, and having the direction of the randomly varying force which we have to consider. We shall set up the equations of motion as in the previous section.

The kinetic energy T is given by

$$T = \int \tfrac{1}{2} \dot{u}^2 \, dm,$$

dm being the element of mass situated at p, the integral being taken over the whole body,

$$= \int \tfrac{1}{2} \left[\sum_r u_r(p) \, \dot{\xi}_r \right]^2 dm = \sum_r \tfrac{1}{2} \int u_r^2(p) \, dm \, \dot{\xi}_r^2$$

$$= \sum_r \tfrac{1}{2} M_r \, \dot{\xi}_r^2, \tag{2}$$

with $M_r = \int u_r^2(p) \, dm.$

The equations of motion are again – if we assume that the damping is hysteretic – of the form

$$\ddot{\xi}_r + (1 + i\eta_r) \, \omega_r^2 \, \xi_r = \frac{\Xi_r}{M_r}, \quad (r = 1, 2, \ldots). \tag{3}$$

The generalised force Ξ_r is to be determined by considering the work done when the point p_P moves through a distance $\delta u(p_P)$. Then

$$\sum_r \Xi_r \, \delta\xi_r = P \cdot \delta u(p_P) = P_0 \, e^{i\omega t} \cdot \sum_r u_r(p_P) \, \delta\xi_r,$$

so that $\Xi_r = P_0 \cdot u_r(p_P) \, e^{i\omega t}.$

Substituting for Ξ_r in (3) and solving we obtain

$$\xi_r = \frac{P_0 \cdot u_r(p_P)}{M_r(\omega_r^2 - \omega^2 + i\eta_r\omega_r^2)} \, e^{i\omega t} :$$

thus, from (1),

$$u(p, t) = \sum_r \frac{P_0 \cdot u_r(p_P) \, u_r(p)}{M_r(\omega_r^2 - \omega^2 + i\eta_r\omega_r^2)} \, e^{i\omega t}. \tag{4}$$

In interpreting (4) the numerator, containing three vector quantities, can only be evaluated in one way: it is of the form $a \cdot bc$, and as bc alone is meaningless the scalar product $a \cdot b$ must be evaluated first. Thus each term of the summation in (4) gives a displacement at any point in the direction of its particular $u_r(p)$.

In this case the receptance will also be a vector quantity: we can define the receptance $\alpha_{1P}(i\omega)$ as the displacement produced at p_1 by a unit force having the same direction as the force P at p_P. To interpret the product $P_0 . u_r(p_P)$ it is convenient to use the notation $[u_r(p_P)]_P$ to indicate the (scalar) magnitude of the component of $u_r(p_P)$ in the direction of P. With this notation

$$P_0 . u_r(p_P) = [u_r(p_P)]_P P_0,$$

so that

$$\alpha_{1P}(i\omega) = \sum_r \frac{[u_r(p_P)]_P \, u_r(p_1)}{M_r(\omega_r^2 - \omega^2 + i\eta_r\omega_r^2)}. \tag{5}$$

So the displacement at any given point is made up of a number of terms each proportional to the normal mode displacement at the point of loading, resolved in the direction of the applied force, and to the normal mode displacement at the given point. Near resonance one of these terms will in general predominate, so that motion at any point will have predominantly the direction of its displacement in the particular normal mode involved.

We see that (5) may be written in terms of actual frequency f and natural frequencies f_r as

$$\alpha_{1P}(if) = \sum_r \mu_r(X_r - iY_r), \tag{6}$$

$$\text{with } \mu_r = \frac{[u_r(p_P)]_P \, u_r(p_1)}{M_r}$$

$$X_r = \frac{f_r^2 - f^2}{4\pi^2[(f_r^2 - f^2)^2 + \eta_r^2 f_r^4]}, \left.\vphantom{\frac{f_r^2}{4\pi^2}}\right\} \tag{7}$$

$$Y_r = \frac{\eta_r f_r^2}{4\pi^2[(f_r^2 - f^2)^2 + \eta_r^2 f_r^4]}.$$

Which are very similar in form to 4.6(6).

If we are interested in the component of displacement measured in a particular direction – as will be so if we record displacement with a single transducer, aligned, let us say, in the x direction – the measured receptance will be given by

$$[\alpha_{1P}(i\omega)]_x = \sum_r \frac{[u_r(p_P)]_P \, [u_r(p_1)]_x}{M_r(\omega_r^2 - \omega^2 + i\eta_r\omega_r^2)}. \tag{8}$$

This we may write in the form of (6) as

$$\alpha(if) = [\alpha_{1P}(if)]_{\mathbf{x}} = \sum_r \mu_r(X_r - iY_r), \qquad (9)$$

where

$$\mu_r = \frac{[\mathbf{u}_r(\mathbf{p}_P)]_P\,[\mathbf{u}_r(\mathbf{p}_1)]_{\mathbf{x}}}{M_r}, \qquad (10)$$

and X_r, Y_r are the expressions of (7).

Using this result there is no difficulty in principle in relating the spectral density $S_1(f)$ of the motion at $\mathbf{p}_1$ in the $\mathbf{x}$ direction to the spectral density $S_P(f)$ of the magnitude of the force $\mathbf{P}(t)$ at $\mathbf{p}_P$ by the usual expression:

$$S_1(f) = |\alpha(if)|^2\,S_P(f).$$

CHAPTER V

RESPONSE INVOLVING CROSS-CORRELATIONS

5.1 Introduction

In the previous chapter where we considered the response of a system to a single randomly varying force, it was shown that a particularly simple relationship, 4.3(3), connected the spectral densities of response and excitation. To determine the spectral density of the response it was only necessary to know the spectral density of the exciting force, and the relevant receptance of the system.

We must now consider more complicated problems in which a number of forces act together. The greater complication here does not arise simply from the greater numbers, but from the possibility that the different forces are in some way related, so that their cross-correlations must be taken into account. Only where it can be shown that forces are quite independent can the effects of cross-correlation be ignored.

Cross-correlation functions and cross spectral densities were introduced in Sections 3.8 and 3.9. In the present chapter we shall investigate the influence of these quantities on response. It is natural to begin by considering the response of a system to two randomly varying forces acting together, as a first step towards the consideration of the distributed random loadings which are a not uncommon feature of random vibration problems in practice.

5.2 Response to Two Random Loadings

Let us consider the response of a system to two random loadings, $P(t)$ and $Q(t)$, acting simultaneously but at different points as in Fig. 5.2-1. Let the resulting displacement of a given point in a given direction be $x(t)$. Suppose the corresponding receptances for harmonic excitation to be α_{xP} and α_{xQ}, and the corresponding weighting functions giving the response to unit impulse to be $W_{xP}(t)$, $W_{xQ}(t)$, extending the notation of Section 4.2 in the obvious way. (In this and later chapters receptances will be represented simply by the symbols α_{xP}, α_{xQ}, etc., rather than by $\alpha_{xP}(if)$, $\alpha_{xQ}(if)$, etc., as pre-

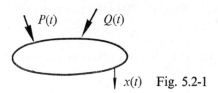

$x(t)$ Fig. 5.2-1

viously, for the sake of brevity and clarity. The subscripts will be chosen where possible to indicate the actual quantities connected rather than their locations.) We would wish, if possible to express the spectral density of $x(t)$ in terms of the spectral densities of $P(t)$ and $Q(t)$. In Section 4.3 we approached the corresponding problem with a single force by way of the autocorrelation functions: we shall endeavour to do the same here.

Suppose that the autocorrelation functions of $x(t)$, $P(t)$, $Q(t)$ are respectively $R_x(\tau)$, $R_P(\tau)$, $R_Q(\tau)$. Then, expanding $x(t)$ and $x(t+\tau)$ as Duhamel integrals, the autocorrelation function of the response $R_x(\tau)$, can be expressed as follows:

$$R_x(\tau) = \langle x(t)\, x(t+\tau)\rangle, \tag{1}$$

$$=\left\langle \int_0^\infty \left[W_{xP}(\tau_1)\, P(t-\tau_1) + W_{xQ}(\tau_1)\, Q(t-\tau_1)\right] d\tau_1 \right.$$

$$\left. \times \int_0^\infty \left[W_{xP}(\tau_2)\, P(t-\tau_2+\tau) + W_{xQ}(\tau_2)\, Q(t-\tau_2+\tau)\right] d\tau_2 \right\rangle$$

$$=\left\langle \int_0^\infty W_{xP}(\tau_1)\, P(t-\tau_1)\, d\tau_1 \int_0^\infty W_{xP}(\tau_2)\, P(t-\tau_2+\tau)\, d\tau_2 \right.$$

$$+ \int_0^\infty W_{xP}(\tau_1)\, P(t-\tau_1)\, d\tau_1 \int_0^\infty W_{xQ}(\tau_2)\, Q(t-\tau_2+\tau)\, d\tau_2$$

$$+ \int_0^\infty W_{xQ}(\tau_1)\, Q(t-\tau_1)\, d\tau_1 \int_0^\infty W_{xP}(\tau_2)\, P(t-\tau_2+\tau)\, d\tau_2$$

$$\left. + \int_0^\infty W_{xQ}(\tau_1)\, Q(t-\tau_1)\, d\tau_1 \int_0^\infty W_{xQ}(\tau_2)\, Q(t-\tau_2+\tau)\, d\tau_2 \right\rangle$$

$$= \int_0^\infty W_{xP}(\tau_1) \left[\int_0^\infty W_{xP}(\tau_2) \langle P(t) \, P(t+\tau_1-\tau_2+\tau) \rangle \, d\tau_2 \right] d\tau_1$$

$$+ \int_0^\infty W_{xP}(\tau_1) \left[\int_0^\infty W_{xQ}(\tau_2) \langle P(t) \, Q(t+\tau_1-\tau_2+\tau) \rangle \, d\tau_2 \right] d\tau_1$$

$$+ \int_0^\infty W_{xQ}(\tau_1) \left[\int_0^\infty W_{xP}(\tau_2) \langle Q(t) \, P(t+\tau_1-\tau_2+\tau) \rangle \, d\tau_2 \right] d\tau_1$$

$$+ \int_0^\infty W_{xQ}(\tau_1) \left[\int_0^\infty W_{xQ}(\tau_2) \langle Q(t) \, Q(t+\tau_1-\tau_2+\tau) \rangle \, d\tau_2 \right] d\tau_1. \tag{2}$$

The meaned quantities in the first and last terms of (2) are simply autocorrelation functions, and may be written as $R_P(\tau_1-\tau_2+\tau)$, $R_Q(\tau_1-\tau_2+\tau)$. The corresponding quantities in the second and third terms are cross-correlation functions such as we have discussed in Sections 3.8 and 3.9: as by definition

$$R_{PQ}(\tau) = \langle P(t) \, Q(t+\tau) \rangle, \tag{3}$$

we can write them as $R_{PQ}(\tau_1-\tau_2+\tau)$ and $R_{QP}(\tau_1-\tau_2+\tau)$ respectively. The autocorrelation function of the response is therefore given by

$$R_x(\tau) = \int_0^\infty W_{xP}(\tau_1) \left[\int_0^\infty W_{xP}(\tau_2) \, R_P(\tau_1-\tau_2+\tau) \, d\tau_2 \right] d\tau_1$$

$$+ \int_0^\infty W_{xP}(\tau_1) \left[\int_0^\infty W_{xQ}(\tau_2) \, R_{PQ}(\tau_1-\tau_2+\tau) \, d\tau_2 \right] d\tau_1$$

$$+ \int_0^\infty W_{xQ}(\tau_1) \left[\int_0^\infty W_{xP}(\tau_2) \, R_{QP}(\tau_1-\tau_2+\tau) \, d\tau_2 \right] d\tau_1$$

$$+ \int_0^\infty W_{xQ}(\tau_1) \left[\int_0^\infty W_{xQ}(\tau_2) \, R_Q(\tau_1-\tau_2+\tau) \, d\tau_2 \right] d\tau_1. \tag{4}$$

It is evidently not possible to derive $R_x(\tau)$ unless $R_{PQ}(\tau)$ and $R_{QP}(\tau)$ are known.

We now have a relationship giving $R_x(\tau)$ in terms of $R_P(\tau)$ and $R_Q(\tau)$ – and of necessity $R_{PQ}(\tau)$ and $R_{QP}(\tau)$ – and so we can proceed just as in Section 4.3 to determine the spectral density of the response by using the Fourier transform relationship between $S_x(f)$ and $R_x(\tau)$. By 3.6(4) we have

$$S_x(f) = 2 \int_{-\infty}^{\infty} R_x(\tau)\, e^{-i2\pi f\tau}\, d\tau: \qquad (5)$$

substitution of (4) in (5), and the use of manipulations exactly similar to those in Section 4.3, leads eventually to

$$S_x(f) = \alpha_{xP}{}^* \alpha_{xP}\, S_P(f) + \alpha_{xP}{}^* \alpha_{xQ}\, S_{PQ}(f) + \\ \alpha_{xQ}{}^* \alpha_{xP}\, S_{QP}(f) + \alpha_{xQ}{}^* \alpha_{xQ}\, S_Q(f), \qquad (6)$$

where the cross spectral density $S_{PQ}(f)$ is given (see 3.8(6)) by

$$S_{PQ}(f) = 2 \int_{-\infty}^{\infty} R_{PQ}(\tau)\, e^{-i2\pi f\tau}\, d\tau. \qquad (7)$$

So the spectral density of the response cannot be determined from a knowledge only of the spectral densities $S_P(f)$ and $S_Q(f)$ of the applied forces: a knowledge of the two cross spectral densities $S_{PQ}(f)$ and $S_{QP}(f)$ is also necessary. Where more than two forces act, there will be correspondingly more cross-correlations to take into account.

We can illustrate the effect of cross-correlation by determining the combined responses due to two randomly varying forces, $P(t)$ and $Q(t)$, considering these to be first quite uncorrelated, and then to be correlated in such a way that $P(t)$ and $Q(t)$ have a constant ratio. The latter case we may, for want of a better word, describe as *direct* correlation.

For no correlation – if $P(t)$ and $Q(t)$ arise from quite independent sources – the cross-correlation functions $R_{PQ}(\tau)$ and $R_{QP}(\tau)$, and so the cross spectral densities $S_{PQ}(f)$ and $S_{QP}(f)$, will be zero. (It is assumed, unless the opposite is obviously implied, that all randomly varying quantities have zero mean value.) Equation (6) then reduces to

$$S_x(f) = |\alpha_{xP}|^2\, S_P(f) + |\alpha_{xQ}|^2\, S_Q(f). \qquad (8)$$

The response spectral density in this case is thus simply the sum of the two response spectral densities obtained with the forces acting separately.

If $P(t)$ and $Q(t)$ are directly correlated, so that $Q(t) = kP(t)$, where k is a constant, then

$$R_{PQ}(\tau) = \langle P(t).kP(t+\tau)\rangle = kR_P(\tau),$$
$$R_{QP}(\tau) = \langle kP(t).P(t+\tau)\rangle = kR_P(\tau),$$
$$R_Q(\tau) = \langle kP(t).kP(t+\tau)\rangle = k^2 R_P(\tau).$$

Using the known relations between correlation functions and spectral densities we have therefore

$$S_{PQ}(f) = kS_P(f), \quad S_{QP}(f) = kS_P(f), \quad S_Q(f) = k^2 S_P(f).$$

Equation (6) now gives

$$S_x(f) = \alpha_{xP}{}^* \alpha_{xP} S_P(f) + \alpha_{xP}{}^* \alpha_{xQ} kS_P(f) + \alpha_{xQ}{}^* \alpha_{xP} kS_p(f) +$$
$$\alpha_{xQ}{}^* \alpha_{xQ} k^2 S_P(f)$$
$$= (\alpha_{xP}{}^* + k\alpha_{xQ}{}^*)(\alpha_{xP} + k\alpha_{xQ}) S_P(f)$$
$$= | \alpha_{xP} + k\alpha_{xQ} |^2 S_P(f).$$

The spectral density of the response now depends on the modulus of a vector sum of the two receptances and so on the relative phase of the two receptances.

Let us consider the case where the spectral densities of the two loadings are identical; that is, where $S_P(f) = S_Q(f) = S(f)$. (Note that this can be so without correlation.) If the forces are uncorrelated we see from equation (8) that

$$S_x(f) = [\, | \alpha_{xP} |^2 + | \alpha_{xQ} |^2 \,] S(f), \tag{9}$$

whereas if the forces are directly correlated, which for $S_P(f) = S_Q(f)$ implies that $k = 1$, we have

$$S_x(f) = | \alpha_{xP} + \alpha_{xQ} |^2 S(f). \tag{10}$$

Equation (10) may be written as

$$S_x(f) = [\, | \alpha_{xP} |^2 + | \alpha_{xQ} |^2 + 2 | \alpha_{xP} || \alpha_{xQ} | \cos\phi\,] S(f), \tag{11}$$

where ϕ is the phase difference between the two receptances at the particular frequency f, and in this form it is more easily compared with (9). Clearly the result for the uncorrelated loadings given by (9) will only be equal to that for the correlated loadings given by (11) when $\cos\phi = 0$; that is, when $\phi = \pm\dfrac{\pi}{2}$. For other values of ϕ the spectral density in the correlated case may have any value between $[\, | \alpha_{xP} | - | \alpha_{xQ} | \,]^2 S(f)$ and $[\, | \alpha_{xP} | + | \alpha_{xQ} | \,]^2 S(f)$ depending on the value of $\cos\phi$. If indeed $\alpha_{xP} = -\alpha_{xQ}$ at some frequency, the spectral density at that frequency in the correlated case will be zero:

for any frequency at which $\alpha_{xP} = \alpha_{xQ}$, the spectral density with correlation will be twice that obtained without it.

These last results could have been inferred without using equation (6) by considering the discrete-frequency response to in-phase and out-of-phase loadings at the two excitation points.

As a further illustrative example we may consider the case where $Q(t)$ reproduces $P(t)$ after a lag of τ_0, so that $Q(t) = P(t+\tau_0)$. In this case

$$R_{PQ}(\tau) = \langle P(t)\, P(t+\tau_0+\tau)\rangle = R_P(\tau_0+\tau).$$

So, using (7),

$$S_{PQ}(f) = 2 \int_{-\infty}^{\infty} R_P(\tau_0+\tau)\, e^{-i2\pi f\tau}\, d\tau$$

$$= 2\, e^{i2\pi f\tau_0} \int_{-\infty}^{\infty} R_P(\tau_0+\tau)\, e^{-i2\pi f(\tau_0+\tau)}\, d(\tau_0+\tau)$$

$$= e^{i2\pi f\tau_0}\, S_P(f).$$

As $S_{QP}(f)$ and $S_{PQ}(f)$ are complex conjugates, we have also

$$S_{QP}(f) = e^{-i2\pi f\tau_0}\, S_P(f),$$

and obviously $S_Q(f) = S_P(f)$.

Equation (6) now becomes

$$S_x(f) = (\alpha_{xP}{}^*\, \alpha_{xP} + e^{i2\pi f\tau_0}\, \alpha_{xP}{}^*\, \alpha_{xQ} +$$
$$e^{-i2\pi f\tau_0}\, \alpha_{xQ}{}^*\, \alpha_{xP} + \alpha_{xQ}{}^*\, \alpha_{xQ})\, S_P(f). \tag{12}$$

5.3 Response to More Than Two Loadings

When more than two random forces act together the analysis of Section 5.2 may be extended without difficulty, although of course the number of cross-correlation terms is greatly increased, and equations become lengthier.

Consider for example the response, $x(t)$, of a system, in a given direction, to three random loadings $P(t)$, $Q(t)$, $R(t)$, acting simultaneously, as shown in Fig. 5.3-1. We can again obtain an expression giving the autocorrelation function $R_x(\tau)$ by expanding $\langle x(t)\, x(t+\tau)\rangle$ in terms of the autocorrelation functions $R_P(\tau)$, $R_Q(\tau)$, $R_R(\tau)$ and the cross-correlation functions $R_{PQ}(\tau)$, $R_{QP}(\tau)$, $R_{QR}(\tau)$, $R_{RQ}(\tau)$, $R_{RP}(\tau)$, $R_{PR}(\tau)$, and this result can be used to express the spectral density

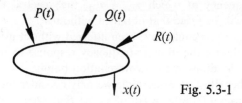

Fig. 5.3-1

$S_x(f)$ of $x(t)$ in terms of the spectral densities and cross spectral densities of the loadings. Proceeding in this way we obtain

$$S_x(f) = \alpha_{xP}^* \alpha_{xP} S_P(f) + \alpha_{xP}^* \alpha_{xQ} S_{PQ}(f) + \alpha_{xP}^* \alpha_{xR} S_{PR}(f)$$
$$+ \alpha_{xQ}^* \alpha_{xQ} S_Q(f) + \alpha_{xQ}^* \alpha_{xR} S_{QR}(f) + \alpha_{xQ}^* \alpha_{xP} S_{QP}(f)$$
$$+ \alpha_{xR}^* \alpha_{xR} S_R(f) + \alpha_{xR}^* \alpha_{xP} S_{RP}(f) + \alpha_{xR}^* \alpha_{xQ} S_{RQ}(f). \quad (1)$$

Where there are n forces $P_1, P_2, \ldots, P_n$ acting, a general result having the form

$$S_x(f) = \sum_{r=1}^{n} \sum_{s=1}^{n} \alpha_{xP_r}^* \alpha_{xP_s} S_{P_rP_s}(f) \quad (2)$$

obviously applies, where $S_{P_rP_r}(f)$ is to be interpreted as $S_{P_r}(f)$. (The symbol $S_{xx}(f)$ is used by some authors to indicate the spectral density of a quantity $x(t)$, and similarly, $R_{xx}(\tau)$ is sometimes preferred to $R_x(\tau)$).

It is not easy to give a general illustration of the effect of the cross-correlation terms, but we can again consider the difference between the response to loadings which have no correlation and the response to similar loadings when direct correlation exists.

Suppose that a body is loaded by three forces $P(t)$, $Q(t)$, $R(t)$, which are quite independent. Then there is no cross-correlation between the loads, and $S_{PQ}(f)$, $S_{QR}(f)$, $S_{RP}(f)$, $S_{QP}(f)$, $S_{RQ}(f)$, $S_{PR}(f)$ are all zero. The spectral density of the displacement $x(t)$ is thus given by

$$S_x(f) = |\alpha_{xP}|^2 S_P(f) + |\alpha_{xQ}|^2 S_Q(f) + |\alpha_{xR}|^2 S_R(f). \quad (3)$$

In the particular case where the spectra are similar, such that

$$S_P(f) = k_P^2 S(f), \quad S_Q(f) = k_Q^2 S(f), \quad S_R(f) = k_R^2 S(f), \text{ then}$$
$$S_x(f) = [k_P^2 |\alpha_{xP}|^2 + k_Q^2 |\alpha_{xQ}|^2 + k_R^2 |\alpha_{xR}|^2] S(f). \quad (4)$$

With no correlation the response is always equal to the sum of the responses for the separate loadings.

If instead direct correlation exists between the loads, we have as before

$$S_P(f) = k_P{}^2 S(f), \ S_Q(f) = k_Q{}^2 S(f), \ S_R(f) = k_R{}^2 S(f),$$

but in addition, now,

$$\left.\begin{array}{l} S_{PQ}(f) = S_{QP}(f) = k_P k_Q \ S(f), \\ S_{QR}(f) = S_{RQ}(f) = k_Q k_R \ S(f), \\ S_{RP}(f) = S_{PR}(f) = k_R k_P \ S(f). \end{array}\right\}$$

Substituting in (1) we obtain

$$S_x(f) = \big[k_P{}^2 \, \alpha_{xP}{}^* \, \alpha_{xP} + k_P k_Q \, \alpha_{xP}{}^* \, \alpha_{xQ} + k_P k_R \, \alpha_{xP}{}^* \, \alpha_{xR}$$
$$+ k_Q{}^2 \, \alpha_{xQ}{}^* \, \alpha_{xQ} + k_Q k_R \, \alpha_{xQ}{}^* \, \alpha_{xR} + k_Q k_P \, \alpha_{xQ}{}^* \, \alpha_{xP}$$
$$+ k_R{}^2 \, \alpha_{xR}{}^* \, \alpha_{xR} + k_R k_P \, \alpha_{xR}{}^* \, \alpha_{xP} + k_R k_Q \, \alpha_{xR}{}^* \, \alpha_{xQ} \big] \, S(f)$$

$$= \big[k_P \, \alpha_{xP}{}^* + k_Q \, \alpha_{xQ}{}^* + k_R \, \alpha_{xR}{}^* \big] \big[k_P \, \alpha_{xP} + k_Q \, \alpha_{xQ} + k_R \, \alpha_{xR} \big] \, S(f)$$

$$= \big| \, k_P \, \alpha_{xP} + k_Q \, \alpha_{xQ} + k_R \, \alpha_{xR} \, \big|^2 \, S(f). \tag{5}$$

Again, when there is correlation between the forces the spectral density of the response at any frequency depends on the relative phase-angles of the receptances, whereas these have no effect on the magnitude of the response when no correlation exists.

5.4 Cross-Correlation of Displacements Due to a Single Force

If we wish to describe the relative motion of two points of a body subjected to a random loading, we must know not only the spectral densities or autocorrelation functions of the separate motions but also their cross spectral densities or cross-correlation functions, as we have seen in Section 3.8. These will exist even when the excitation consists of a single randomly varying force. Apart from the intrinsic interest of this problem the present discussion will provide in analytical form some typical examples of cross-correlation functions and cross spectral densities.

Consider a body excited by a single randomly varying force $P(t)$, which has autocorrelation function $R_P(\tau)$ and spectral density $S_P(f)$. Suppose that as a result of this loading two points on the body have displacements $x(t), y(t)$, and that these have autocorrelation functions $R_x(\tau), R_y(\tau)$ and spectral densities $S_x(f), S_y(f)$ respectively.

The spectral densities of the displacements are related to that of the force by the equations

$$S_x(f) = \left| \alpha_{xP} \right|^2 S_P(f), \left.\begin{array}{l}\\\\\end{array}\right\}$$
$$S_y(f) = \left| \alpha_{yP} \right|^2 S_P(f), \tag{1}$$

where α_{xP}, α_{yP} are the corresponding receptances giving the responses for harmonic excitation.

We have seen, in Section 4.2, that

$$\alpha_{xP} = \int_0^\infty W_{xP}(\tau)\, e^{-i2\pi f\tau}\, d\tau, \left.\begin{array}{l}\\\\\\\\\end{array}\right\}$$
$$\alpha_{yP} = \int_0^\infty W_{yP}(\tau)\, e^{-i2\pi f\tau}\, d\tau, \tag{2}$$

where $W_{xP}(\tau)$, $W_{yP}(\tau)$ are weighting functions giving the response to unit-impulse loadings, so that

$$x(t) = \int_0^\infty W_{xP}(\tau)\, P(t-\tau)\, d\tau, \left.\begin{array}{l}\\\\\\\\\end{array}\right\}$$
$$y(t) = \int_0^\infty W_{yP}(\tau)\, P(t-\tau)\, d\tau. \tag{3}$$

Equations (2) and (3) together with our knowledge of the Fourier transform relationship between $S_P(f)$ and $R_P(\tau)$ enable us to obtain expressions for $R_{xy}(\tau)$ and $S_{xy}(f)$. We have
$$R_{xy}(\tau) = \langle x(t)\, y(t+\tau) \rangle$$

$$= \left\langle \int_0^\infty W_{xP}(\tau_1)\, P(t-\tau_1)\, d\tau_1 \int_0^\infty W_{yP}(\tau_2)\, P(t+\tau-\tau_2)\, d\tau_2 \right\rangle$$

$$= \int_0^\infty W_{xP}(\tau_1) \left[\int_0^\infty W_{yP}(\tau_2)\, \langle P(t-\tau_1)\, P(t+\tau-\tau_2) \rangle\, d\tau_2 \right] d\tau_1$$

$$= \int_0^\infty W_{xP}(\tau_1) \left[\int_0^\infty W_{yP}(\tau_2)\, \langle P(t)\, P(t+\tau+\tau_1-\tau_2) \rangle\, d\tau_2 \right] d\tau_1$$

$$= \int_0^\infty W_{xP}(\tau_1) \left[\int_0^\infty W_{yP}(\tau_2)\, R_P(\tau+\tau_1-\tau_2)\, d\tau_2 \right] d\tau_1. \tag{4}$$

This is explicit, though not easy to interpret.

The cross spectral density $S_{xy}(f)$ can be obtained from (4) by using the Fourier transform relationship between $S_{xy}(f)$ and $R_{xy}(\tau)$. Thus

$$S_{xy}(f) = 2\int_{-\infty}^{\infty} R_{xy}(\tau)\, e^{-i2\pi f\tau} d\tau$$

$$= 2\int_{-\infty}^{\infty}\left\{\int_{0}^{\infty} W_{xP}(\tau_1)\left[\int_{0}^{\infty} W_{yP}(\tau_2)R_P(\tau+\tau_1-\tau_2)d\tau_2\right]d\tau_1\right\} e^{-i2\pi f\tau} d\tau$$

$$= 2\int_{0}^{\infty} W_{xP}(\tau_1)\, e^{i2\pi f\tau_1}\left[\int_{0}^{\infty} W_{yP}(\tau_2)\, e^{-i2\pi f\tau_2}\right.$$

$$\left.\left(\int_{-\infty}^{\infty} R_P(\tau+\tau_1-\tau_2)\, e^{-i2\pi f(\tau+\tau_1-\tau_2)}d\tau\right)d\tau_2\right]d\tau_1$$

$$= 2\int_{0}^{\infty} W_{xP}(\tau_1)\, e^{i2\pi f\tau_1}d\tau_1 \int_{0}^{\infty} W_{yP}(\tau_2)\, e^{-i2\pi f\tau_2}d\tau_2$$

$$\times \int_{-\infty}^{\infty} R_P(\tau+\tau_1-\tau_2)\, e^{-i2\pi f(\tau+\tau_1-\tau_2)}\, d(\tau+\tau_1-\tau_2)$$

$$= 2\, \alpha_{xP}{}^* \, \alpha_{yP}\, \tfrac{1}{2}S_P(f)$$

$$= \alpha_{xP}{}^* \, \alpha_{yP}\, S_P(f). \tag{5}$$

It follows from (5) that $S_{yx}(f)$, being the complex conjugate of $S_{xy}(f)$, is given by

$$S_{yx}(f) = \alpha_{yP}{}^* \, \alpha_{xP}\, S_P(f). \tag{6}$$

These results reduce to (1) in the special case where x and y coincide.

We can demonstrate the application of this theory by considering the cross-correlation of the displacements of two points on a beam which is excited by a single randomly varying load.

Consider as before a beam (Fig. 5.4-1) whose normal modes are $w_r(x)$ and whose natural frequencies are f_r. Assume that the mass per unit length is m, so that the generalised mass M_r in each mode is $\int_{0}^{l} w_r{}^2(x)\, m\, dx$, and that the damping is such as to be expressible by multiplying the generalised stiffness by a complex factor $(1+i\eta_r)$. We shall determine the cross spectral density $S_{12}(f)$ of the displacements $w(x_1, t)$, $w(x_2, t)$, of the two points $x = x_1$ and $x = x_2$, due to a force $P(t)$ acting at $x = x_P$. We shall denote by α_{1P}, α_{2P} the receptances giving the corresponding motions at x_1, x_2 in response to harmonic excitation at x_P.

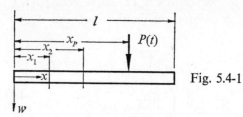

Fig. 5.4-1

The receptances α_{1P}, α_{2P} will be of the form given in 4.6(6). We have therefore

$$\alpha_{1P} = \sum_r \mu_{r(1)} (X_r - iY_r), \tag{7}$$

where

$$\mu_{r(1)} = \frac{w_r(x_1)\, w_r(x_P)}{M_r}$$

$$\left.\begin{array}{l} X_r = \dfrac{f_r^2 - f^2}{4\pi^2[(f_r^2 - f^2)^2 + \eta_r^2 f_r^4]} \\[3mm] Y_r = \dfrac{\eta_r f_r^2}{4\pi^2[(f_r^2 - f^2)^2 + \eta_r^2 f_r^4]}, \end{array}\right\} \tag{8}$$

and $\alpha_{2P} = \sum_r \mu_{r(2)} (X_r - iY_r),$ \hfill (9)

where

$$\mu_{r(2)} = \frac{w_r(x_2)\, w_r(x_P)}{M_r} \tag{10}$$

and X_r, Y_r are exactly as in equations (8).

If therefore the spectral density of the force $P(t)$ is $S_P(f)$, the cross spectral density of $w(x_1, t)$ and $w(x_2, t)$ may be written, using (5), as

$$S_{12}(f) = \left[\sum_r \mu_{r(1)}(X_r + iY_r) \right]\left[\sum_r \mu_{r(2)}(X_r - iY_r) \right] S_P(f). \tag{11}$$

This can be expanded to give

$$S_{12}(f) = \Bigg[\sum_r \mu_{r(1)} X_r \sum_r \mu_{r(2)} X_r + \sum_r \mu_{r(1)} Y_r \sum_r \mu_{r(2)} Y_r$$

$$- i\left(\sum_r \mu_{r(1)} X_r \sum_r \mu_{r(2)} Y_r - \sum_r \mu_{r(1)} Y_r \sum_r \mu_{r(2)} X_r \right) \Bigg] S_P(f),$$

$$\tag{12}$$

and it is in general complex, unless $\mu_{r(1)} = \mu_{r(2)}$. Equation (12) gives the exact expression for $S_{12}(f)$, and cannot be simplified further because of the product terms. $S_{21}(f)$ is simply the complex conjugate of (12).

There is, as in 4.6, scope for developing a very much simpler approximate result if the damping is small, and the peaks of response receptances are well separated. In such a case large motions in each of the modes will only occur when f has a value close to the corresponding natural frequency. Thus for any value of f, large contributions can only arise from a single term of each of the summations, and so in each product of two summations, terms such as X_r^2 and $X_r Y_r$ will always predominate over product terms such as $X_r X_s$ and $X_r Y_s$. In such a case it is permissible to neglect these product terms and to write (12) as

$$
S_{12}(f) = \left[\sum_r \mu_{r(1)}\,\mu_{r(2)}\,X_r^2 + \sum_r \mu_{r(1)}\,\mu_{r(2)}\,Y_r^2 \right.
$$
$$
\left. -i\left(\sum_r \mu_{r(1)}\,\mu_{r(2)}\,X_r Y_r - \sum_r \mu_{r(1)}\,\mu_{r(2)}\,Y_r X_r \right) \right] S_P(f)
$$
$$
= \left[\sum_r \mu_{r(1)}\,\mu_{r(2)}\,(X_r^2 + Y_r^2) \right] S_P(f). \tag{13}
$$

The imaginary part is now negligible in comparison with the real part, and the cross spectral density is effectively real. It follows that $S_{21}(f) = S_{12}(f)$.

We may note that when the two points x_1 and x_2 coincide, (13) reduces to either

$$
\left.
\begin{aligned}
S_1(f) &= \left[\sum_r \mu_{r(1)}^2\,(X_r^2 + Y_r^2) \right] S_P(f) \\
\text{or } S_2(f) &= \left[\sum_r \mu_{r(2)}^2\,(X_r^2 + Y_r^2) \right] S_P(f),
\end{aligned}
\right\} \tag{14}
$$

which agree with the approximate result obtained in Section 4.6.

We can now, if we wish, make use of (13) to determine the spectral density of the difference between $w(x_1, t)$ and $w(x_2, t)$. This spectral density which we may write as $S_{(w_1-w_2)}(f)$, is given by

$$
S_{(w_1-w_2)}(f) = S_1(f) - S_{12}(f) - S_{21}(f) + S_2(f), \text{ by 3.8(5),}
$$
$$
= \sum_r \left[(\mu_{r(1)}^2 - \mu_{r(1)}\mu_{r(2)} - \mu_{r(2)}\mu_{r(1)} + \mu_{r(2)}^2)(X_r^2 + Y_r^2) \right] S_P(f)
$$

$$= \sum_r \left[(\mu_{r(1)} - \mu_{r(2)})^2 (X_r^2 + Y_r^2) \right] S_P(f)$$

$$= \sum_r \left[\left(\frac{[w_r(x_1) - w_r(x_2)]\, w_r(x_P)}{M_r} \right)^2 \times \frac{1}{16\pi^4 \left[(f_r^2 - f^2)^2 + \eta_r^2 f_r^4 \right]} \right]$$

$$S_P(f). \tag{15}$$

Extension of these results to the general case of a body in three dimensions can be made on the lines of Section 4.7.

Similar analysis can be carried out to determine the cross spectral density $S_{xy}(f)$ between two displacements $x(t)$ and $y(t)$ where there are two or more loadings $P(t)$, $Q(t)$, etc. With the obvious extensions of notation and using the same methods of analysis it can be shown that

$$S_{xy}(f) = \alpha_{xP}{}^* \alpha_{yP}\, S_P(f) + \alpha_{xP}{}^* \alpha_{yQ}\, S_{PQ}(f) + \\ \alpha_{xQ}{}^* \alpha_{yP}\, S_{QP}(f) + \alpha_{xQ}{}^* \alpha_{yQ}\, S_Q(f). \tag{16}$$

This reduces to the expected results in the simpler cases where the loads P, Q, or the displacements x, y, coincide.

Where there are n forces $P_1, P_2, \ldots, P_n$ the corresponding result for the displacement cross spectral density is

$$S_{xy}(f) = \sum_{r=1}^{n} \sum_{s=1}^{n} \alpha_{xP_r}{}^* \alpha_{yP_s}\, S_{P_r P_s}(f). \tag{17}$$

5.5 Cross-Correlation of Excitation and Response

Cross-correlation of two randomly varying quantities is to be expected when they derive to any extent from the same source. In the last section, for example, we considered the cross-correlation of the displacements of two points of a body subjected to a given excitation.

But cross-correlation is obviously also to be expected between two quantities which are related in themselves. In this section we investigate, not the correlation of two effects due to the same cause, but the correlation of cause and effect – the cross-correlation of a randomly varying force applied to a system and a displacement resulting from this excitation. This analysis will of course be equally well applicable to the cross correlations of the input and output of any linear system.

Suppose that the randomly varying force $P(t)$ acting on a body at one point gives rise to a displacement $x(t)$ in a given direction at another point (Fig. 5.5-1). Let the corresponding responses in

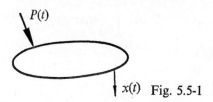

$x(t)$ Fig. 5.5-1

respect of harmonic and unit-impulse excitation be given by the receptance α_{xP} and weighting function $W_{xP}(\tau)$. We shall determine first the cross-correlation function of the randomly varying $P(t)$ and $x(t)$.

Using arguments similar to those of 4.3 we have

$$
\begin{aligned}
R_{Px}(\tau) &= \langle P(t)\, x(t+\tau)\rangle \\
&= \left\langle P(t) \int_0^\infty W_{xP}(\tau_1)\, P(t+\tau-\tau_1)\, d\tau_1 \right\rangle, \quad \text{by 4.2(13)}, \\
&= \int_0^\infty W_{xP}(\tau_1)\, \langle P(t)\, P(t+\tau-\tau_1)\rangle\, d\tau_1 \\
&= \int_0^\infty W_{xP}(\tau_1)\, R_P(\tau-\tau_1)\, d\tau_1.
\end{aligned}
\tag{1}
$$

Equation (1) gives the required cross-correlation function in terms of the autocorrelation function of the exciting force and the weighting function.

Having now obtained $R_{Px}(\tau)$ we can use our result to obtain the cross-spectral density $S_{Px}(f)$. We have, by definition,

$$
S_{Px}(f) = 2 \int_{-\infty}^\infty R_{Px}(\tau)\, e^{-i2\pi f\tau}\, d\tau
$$

$$
= 2 \int_{-\infty}^\infty \left[\int_0^\infty W_{xP}(\tau_1)\, R_P(\tau-\tau_1)\, d\tau_1 \right] e^{-i2\pi f\tau}\, d\tau
$$

$$
= 2 \int_0^\infty W_{xP}(\tau_1) \left[\int_{-\infty}^\infty R_P(\tau-\tau_1)\, e^{-i2\pi f\tau}\, d\tau \right] d\tau_1
$$

$$
= 2 \int_0^\infty W_{xP}(\tau_1)\, e^{-i2\pi f\tau_1} \left[\int_{-\infty}^\infty R_P(\tau-\tau_1)\, e^{-i2\pi f(\tau-\tau_1)}\, d\tau \right] d\tau_1
$$

$$= 2 \int_0^\infty W_{xP}(\tau_1) \, e^{-i2\pi f \tau_1} \, d\tau_1 \int_{-\infty}^\infty R_P(\tau - \tau_1) \, e^{-i2\pi f(\tau - \tau_1)} \, d(\tau - \tau_1)$$

$$= 2 \, \alpha_{xP} \, \tfrac{1}{2} S_P(f)$$

$$= \alpha_{xP} \, S_P(f). \tag{2}$$

So the cross spectral density is simply the product of the receptance and the spectral density of the exciting force.

We know that $S_{xP}(f)$ is the complex conjugate of $S_{Px}(f)$, so that

$$S_{xP}(f) = \alpha_{xP}{}^* \, S_P(f). \tag{3}$$

We can also derive these cross spectral densities in terms of the direct spectral density of the response. Multiplying (2) by $\alpha_{xP}{}^*$ we obtain

$$\begin{aligned} \alpha_{xP}{}^* \, S_{Px}(f) &= \alpha_{xP}{}^* \, \alpha_{xP} \, S_P(f) \\ &= |\alpha_{xP}|^2 \, S_P(f) \\ &= S_x(f). \end{aligned}$$

Thus

$$S_{Px}(f) = \frac{1}{\alpha_{xP}{}^*} \, S_x(f). \tag{4}$$

It is interesting to consider the cross-correlations of excitation and response when there is a white noise excitation. For $S_P(f) = S_1$, independent of frequency, the cross spectral density is given by

$$S_{Px}(f) = \alpha_{xP} \, S_1. \tag{5}$$

The cross spectral density thus has the exact form of the receptance. As the receptance is complex, phase differences being indicated as phase changes of the complex quantity, the cross spectral density is complex also. (The direct response spectral density, $S_x(f)$, is of course proportional to $|\alpha_{xP}|^2$ and always independent of phase.)

The cross-correlation function of excitation and response for white noise excitation can be found by using the fact that for white noise of uniform spectral density S_1, $R(\tau) = \tfrac{1}{2} S_1 \, \delta(\tau)$, where $\delta(\tau)$ is the Dirac δ-function. (See Section 3.6.) Using equation (1) we have

$$\begin{aligned} R_{Px}(\tau) &= \int_0^\infty W_{xP}(\tau_1) \, R_P(\tau - \tau_1) \, d\tau_1 \\ &= \int_0^\infty W_{xP}(\tau_1) \, \tfrac{1}{2} S_1 \, \delta(\tau - \tau_1) \, d\tau_1. \end{aligned}$$

Because of the form of the δ-function the integral need only be taken over an infinitesimal region about $\tau_1 = \tau$, giving

$$R_{Px}(\tau) = \tfrac{1}{2}S_1 W_{xP}(\tau). \tag{6}$$

For white noise excitation, therefore, the cross-correlation function of excitation and response has exactly the form of the weighting function $W_{xP}(\tau)$.

These results may in certain circumstances offer a good method of determining the vibration characteristics of a system experimentally. Equation (2), for example, would give both modulus and phase of α_{xP} if $S_{Px}(f)$ and $S_P(f)$ were measured, whereas comparison of $S_P(f)$ and $S_x(f)$ would give no information about phase. With white noise excitation, measurement of $R_{Px}(\tau)$ would give the weighting function $W_{xP}(\tau)$.

5.6 Response to Distributed Loadings

In practice random vibration is often excited by randomly varying pressures acting over the whole surface of a body. The analysis of response which we have developed in the last two chapters apparently equips us only to treat simple or multiple point loads, and we must now show how our results can be extended to deal with distributed loads. Several special cases of practical interest come to mind in which the cross-correlation between the pressures at different points has a particularly simple form and so permits a simplified analysis: there may for example be direct correlation so that all pressures are proportional to a single randomly varying quantity, or the pressures may be quite uncorrelated so that the pressure at any point is independent of that at any other. It will be more convenient, however, to obtain results for the general case first, and then to use these results to treat special cases. It will be sufficient in considering response to distributed loading to restrict our attention to the case of a beam: the analysis for a beam will show all the essential features of that for more complicated systems; extension after the manner of Section 4.7 to deal with the more general case presents no difficulty in principle.

General Case. Consider a beam of length l as in Fig. 5.6-1 subject to a distributed loading of intensity $p(x, t)$ per unit length. We wish to determine the response $w(x_1, t)$ at $x = x_1$: in the analysis it will be convenient to refer to loadings at two representative positions $x = x_A$ and $x = x_B$: we can for example denote receptances by

RV G

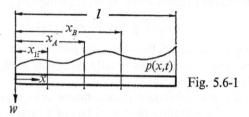

Fig. 5.6-1

α_{1A}, α_{1B} (giving the response at x_1 to point loading $e^{i\omega t}$ at x_A, x_B respectively). In specifying cross spectral densities or cross-correlation functions it becomes necessary to adopt a more explicit set of symbols which will distinguish between displacements and pressures. We shall therefore use $S_w(x_A, x_B; f)$ to represent the cross spectral density of the displacements $w(x_A, t)$, $w(x_B, t)$, and $S_p(x_A, x_B; f)$ to represent the cross spectral density of the pressures $p(x_A, t), p(x_B, t)$; direct spectral densities will be denoted by $S_w(x_A, f)$, $S_p(x_A, f)$, etc.; the corresponding cross-correlation and autocorrelation functions will be denoted by $R_w(x_A, x_B; \tau)$, $R_p(x_A, x_B; \tau)$, $R_w(x_A, \tau)$, $R_p(x_A, \tau)$, etc.

The cross-correlation function and cross spectral density of the pressures are, by definition,

$$R_p(x_A, x_B; \tau) = \langle p(x_A, t)\, p(x_B, t+\tau)\rangle,$$
$$\text{and } S_p(x_A, x_B; f) = 2 \int_{-\infty}^{\infty} R_p(x_A, x_B; \tau)\, e^{-i2\pi f\tau}\, d\tau. \tag{1}$$

The response can be expressed in terms of these quantities by extending the results of Section 5.3 which show that with discrete loadings $P_1, P_2, \ldots$, acting at points $x_{P_1}, x_{P_2}, \ldots$, the spectral density of the motion $w(x_1, t)$ is given by

$$S_w(x_1, f) = \sum_{r=1}^{\infty} \sum_{s=1}^{\infty} \alpha_{x_1 P_r}{}^* \alpha_{x_1 P_s} S_{P_r P_s}(f). \tag{2}$$

Here the α's are the receptances giving the displacement of x_1 due to harmonic loadings at x_{P_r}, x_{P_s} and $S_{P_r P_s}(f)$ is the cross spectral density of these forces.

For a distributed load the discrete forces P_r, P_s must be replaced by loadings $p(x_A, t)dx_A$, $p(x_B, t)dx_B$ at x_A, x_B. The autocorrelation function of these loadings is now

$$\langle p(x_A, t)\, dx_A\, p(x_B, t+\tau)\, dx_B \rangle = \langle p(x_A, t)\, p(x_B, t+\tau) \rangle\, dx_A\, dx_B$$
$$= R_p(x_A, x_B; \tau)\, dx_A\, dx_B,$$

and the cross spectral density is therefore $S_p(x_A, x_B; f)\, dx_A\, dx_B$.

Applying now (2), in which the two summation signs must be replaced by integrals, we obtain

$$S_w(x_1, f) = \int_0^l \int_0^l \alpha_{1A}{}^* \, \alpha_{1B}\, S_p(x_A, x_B; f)\, dx_A\, dx_B. \qquad (3)$$

The receptances α_{1A}, α_{1B} which give the response at x_1 to harmonic loading at x_A, x_B are of course functions of x_A, x_B, respectively.

The result (3) gives the spectral density of the motion at any point in terms of the cross spectral densities of the loading, and of the receptances of the system. It is probably in its most useful form as it stands, but it can be expanded by expressing the receptances in terms of the normal mode shapes and system constants in the usual way. As, by 4.6(6)

$$\alpha_{1A} = \sum_r \frac{w_r(x_1)\, w_r(x_A)}{4\pi^2 M_r(f_r^2 - f^2 + i\eta_r f_r^2)},$$

we can write (3) as

$$S_w(x_1, f) = \int_0^l \int_0^l \sum_r \frac{w_r(x_1)\, w_r(x_A)}{4\pi^2 M_r(f_r^2 - f^2 - i\eta_r f_r^2)}$$
$$\times \sum_s \frac{w_s(x_1)\, w_s(x_B)}{4\pi^2 M_s(f_s^2 - f^2 + i\eta_s f_s^2)} \times S_p(x_A, x_B; f)\, dx_A\, dx_B$$
$$= \sum_r \sum_s \frac{w_r(x_1)\, w_s(x_1)}{16\pi^4\, M_r\, M_s\, (f_r^2 - f^2 - i\eta_r f_r^2)(f_s^2 - f^2 + i\eta_s f_s^2)}$$
$$\times \int_0^l \int_0^l w_r(x_A)\, w_s(x_B)\, S_p(x_A, x_B; f)\, dx_A\, dx_B. \qquad (4)$$

If the damping is small enough and the peaks are well separated, we can approximate by neglecting the product terms and obtain the much simpler expression

$$S_w(x_1, f) = \sum_r \left[\frac{w_r^2(x_1)}{16\pi^4 M_r^2 [(f_r^2 - f^2)^2 + \eta_r^2 f_r^4]} \int_0^l \int_0^l w_r(x_A)\, w_r(x_B) \right.$$
$$\left. S_p(x_A, x_B; f)\, dx_A\, dx_B \vphantom{\int} \right]. \qquad (5)$$

It is also possible to obtain a result corresponding to (3) giving the cross spectral density of the displacements due to a distributed loading. Extending 5.4(17), which gives the cross spectral density of the displacements due to discrete loads, in exactly the same way leads to

$$S(x_1, x_2; f) = \int_0^l \int_0^l \alpha_{1A}^* \, \alpha_{2B} \, S(x_A, x_B; f) \, dx_A \, dx_B. \quad (6)$$

This differs only from (3) in its receptances, and results corresponding to (4) and (5) can be written down very easily if required.

Special Cases. We have until now made no assumption about the way in which the loading intensities at different points are correlated: we have assumed only that there is a stationary cross-correlation between the intensities at any two points, and that this can be described by means of the cross spectral density $S_p(x_A, x_B; f)$ for every pair of points x_A, x_B. We shall now make use of Equation (3) to obtain results giving the spectral density of the motion when the cross-correlation of the loading intensity has certain particular forms which are of special interest.

We can first show that (3) gives correct results for a single point loading $P(t)$, acting at $x = x_P$, and of spectral density $S_P(f)$. The pressure can be represented here by

$$p(x, t) = P(t) \, \delta(x - x_P),$$

so that

$$\begin{aligned} R_p(x_A, x_B; \tau) &= \langle P(t) \, \delta(x_A - x_P) \, P(t+\tau) \, \delta(x_B - x_P) \rangle \\ &= R_P(\tau) \, \delta(x_A - x_P) \, \delta(x_B - x_P), \end{aligned}$$

and so

$$S_p(x_A, x_P; f) = S_P(f) \, \delta(x_A - x_P) \, \delta(x_B - x_P). \quad (7)$$

Substituting in (3) we obtain

$$\begin{aligned} S_w(x_1, f) &= \int_0^l \int_0^l \alpha_{1A}^* \, \alpha_{1B} \, S_P(f) \, \delta(x_A - x_P) \, \delta(x_B - x_P) \, dx_A \, dx_B \\ &= \int_0^l \alpha_{1A}^* \, \delta(x_A - x_P) \, dx_A \int_0^l \alpha_{1B} \, \delta(x_B - x_P) \, dx_B \, S_P(f) \\ &= \alpha_{1P}^* \, \alpha_{1P} \, S_P(f), \quad (8) \end{aligned}$$

agreeing exactly with 4.3(3).

When there is direct correlation, so that the loading intensities at all points vary proportionally to a single randomly varying quantity $\phi(t)$, we can express the loading intensity as

$$p(x, t) = p_0(x)\, \phi(t).$$

It follows that

$$R_p(x_A, x_B; \tau) = \langle p_0(x_A)\, \phi(t)\, p_0(x_B)\, \phi(t+\tau)\rangle$$
$$= p_0(x_A)\, p_0(x_B)\, R_\phi(\tau),$$

and so, that

$$S_p(x_A, x_B; f) = p_0(x_A)\, p_0(x_B)\, S_\phi(f). \tag{9}$$

Substituting in (3) we obtain

$$
\begin{aligned}
S_w(x_1, f) &= \int_0^l \int_0^l \alpha_{1A}{}^* \, \alpha_{1B}\, p_0(x_A)\, p_0(x_B)\, S_\phi(f)\, dx_A\, dx_B \\
&= \int_0^l \alpha_{1A}{}^* \, p_0(x_A)\, dx_A \int_0^l \alpha_{1B}\, p_0(x_B)\, dx_B\, S_\phi(f) \\
&= \left| \int_0^l \alpha_{1A}\, p_0(x_A)\, dx_A \right|^2 S_\phi(f).
\end{aligned}
\tag{10}
$$

When there is no cross-correlation at all between loading intensities, the cross spectral density is expressible as

$$S_p(x_A, x_B; f) = S(x_A, f)\, \delta(x_A - x_B) \tag{11}$$

(the δ-function has zero value except when $x_A = x_B$).
Substituting in (3) we obtain

$$
\begin{aligned}
S_w(x_1, f) &= \int_0^l \int_0^l \alpha_{1A}{}^* \, \alpha_{1B}\, S(x_A, f)\, \delta(x_A - x_B)\, dx_A\, dx_B \\
&= \int_0^l \alpha_{1B} \left[\int_0^l \alpha_{1A}{}^* \, S(x_A, f)\, \delta(x_A - x_B)\, dx_A \right] dx_B \\
&= \int_0^l \alpha_{1B} \left[\alpha_{1B}{}^* \, S(x_B, f) \right] dx_B \\
&= \int_0^l |\alpha_{1B}|^2 \, S(x_B, f)\, dx_B.
\end{aligned}
\tag{12}
$$

As a final example, let us consider the case where a randomly distributed pressure field moves past our body at a constant velocity, so that different points experience the same randomly varying pressure but with time-lags corresponding to their position. In such a case

$$p(x_B, t) = p(x_A, t + \tau_0),$$

where $\quad \tau_0 = \dfrac{x_B - x_A}{v}.$

It follows that $\quad R_p(x_A, x_B; \tau) = \langle p(x_A, t) \, p(x_A, t + \tau_0 + \tau) \rangle$
$$= R_p(\tau_0 + \tau),$$

where $R_p(\tau)$ is the autocorrelation function at all points. Then

$$S_p(x_A, x_B; f) = 2 \int_{-\infty}^{\infty} R_p(\tau_0 + \tau) \, e^{-i2\pi f \tau} \, d\tau, \qquad \text{by (1),}$$

$$= 2 \, e^{i2\pi f \tau_0} \int_{-\infty}^{\infty} R_p(\tau_0 + \tau) \, e^{-i2\pi f(\tau_0 + \tau)} \, d(\tau_0 + \tau)$$

$$= e^{i2\pi f \tau_0} \, S_p(f). \qquad (13)$$

Substituting in (3) we obtain

$$S_w(x_1, f) = \int_0^l \int_0^l \alpha_{1A}{}^* \, \alpha_{1B} \, e^{i2\pi f(x_B - x_A)/v} \, S_p(f) \, dx_A \, dx_B$$

$$= \int_0^l \alpha_{1A}{}^* \, e^{-i2\pi f x_A/v} \, dx_A \int_0^l \alpha_{1B} \, e^{i2\pi f x_B/v} \, dx_B \, S_p(f)$$

$$= \left| \int_0^l \alpha_{1A} \, e^{i2\pi f x_A/v} \, dx_A \right|^2 S_p(f). \qquad (14)$$

The results (8), (10), (12), (14) have been left with the receptances unexpanded. Expressions giving the same results expanded in terms of mode shapes and system constants can be obtained easily enough either by substituting for the receptances or by carrying out instead the integrations of (4) or (5).

In these few simple examples we have obviously not exhausted the cases which are of practical interest and for which analysis is possible. For further examples the reader is referred to references 8, 10, 12, 16, 22.

CHAPTER VI

PEAK DISTRIBUTION AND ENVELOPE FLUCTUATION

6.1 Introduction

In this chapter we shall consider certain further characteristics of a randomly varying quantity which are of some practical importance. We have already considered the probability distribution of the quantity itself but we shall see that it is the way in which the peaks of a stress record are distributed with respect to time which is relevant to the calculation of the expected life of a component, and so to the probability of failure within a given service life. We must consider in how far this distribution can be predicted by means of the concepts at our disposal.

When we examine the signal emerging from a narrow band filter the differing heights of the successive peaks define a fluctuating envelope whose own probability density can be defined in terms of the variance of the signal. When such a filter is used to measure the spectral density of a signal, using a record of finite length, the fluctuations in amplitude give rise to a considerable scatter in the measured values of spectral density. We shall see that the variance of these values can be determined theoretically.

6.2 Failure Due to Random Loading

In the earlier chapters of this book we discussed the essential characteristics of random processes, and saw how they could be described with some precision, in spite of their random nature. We saw, for example, that a single randomly varying force could be described by specifying its spectral density, and that several such forces acting simultaneously could be described by means of their spectral densities and cross spectral densities. We then developed analysis which enabled us to describe in the same way the motion in any given system in response to such loadings. If the loadings were Gaussian (or nearly so) the motions would be Gaussian also, and in this case their whole probability distribution would be determinable from the spectral density or autocorrelation function. If the resulting displacements were so described, the strains, and consequently the stresses, could easily be described in the same way.

With the stresses arising in response to a specified random loading determinable to this extent, it might seem that the problem of calculating whether a particular component or structure would fail during its service life was practically solved. But this is not the case, even if we assume that the applied loads can be described with any precision, which is rarely so at the design stage.

There are two difficulties: firstly no criterion of failure exists which describes adequately the mechanical properties under randomly varying stress conditions, and secondly our description of stress in terms of its spectral density or probability density is not readily applicable to such criteria as do exist. In time, no doubt, the failure of materials under randomly varying loads will be fully understood, but meanwhile we must accept such approximate criteria of failure as are available: a common criterion is that due to Miner, and this we shall shortly introduce. We must also develop the means for applying it, and we shall see that this will call for a knowledge of the distribution, not of the randomly varying stress, but of its peak values. We must consider in how far this distribution can be expressed in terms of the quantities which we have already defined.

For the purpose of this book the absence of a valid criterion of failure is no great disadvantage. It is not so much our intention to obtain valid design formulae as to show how our concepts can be combined with a given criterion to obtain an estimate of the probability of failure. Usually a highly accurate determination is not justified by the accuracy with which the applied forces can be described.

We should remember that the failure of equipment due to random vibration does not necessarily imply the mechanical failure of a component due to its being overloaded. Failure may result indirectly because some vital part is rendered incapable of functioning correctly: the incorrect functioning of a relay or electrical circuit in a control system can render a complete equipment ineffective without permanently damaging any component. We shall however confine ourselves for the present to discussing mechanical failure.

When a steady stress acts in a component, failure may be assumed – with sufficient accuracy for our purposes – to occur when the stress is increased beyond a certain critical value. But a stress above this value will not necessarily cause failure if it is applied suddenly and for a very brief period of time: the conditions then are more complicated and the process is less well understood. If the applied stress varies harmonically with an amplitude less than the ultimate strength of the material, failure occurs – if at all – after a number of cycles of stress which depends on the mean value of the stress, on the amplitude of fluctuation, and on the properties of the material.

Where the stress history does not consist of repeated cycles of a stress of constant amplitude $\pm s$ leading to failure after N_f cycles, but of a sequence with N_1 cycles at $\pm s_1$, followed by N_2 cycles at $\pm s_2$, and so on, it has been suggested that the proportion of the total damage incurred at each stress level is equal to the ratio which the number of cycles of stress at that level bears to the total possible number of stress cycles at that level. Thus if N_r is the actual number of cycles of a stress of $\pm s_r$, and N_{rf} cycles would be sufficient to cause failure, the damage at that level is N_r/N_{rf}, and final failure occurs when damage is complete – that is, for a loading history involving n different stress levels, when

$$\sum_{r=1}^{n} \frac{N_r}{N_{rf}} = 1. \tag{1}$$

This is known as the Miner criterion (reference 18): it is in many ways unsatisfactory, but it has the advantage of simplicity and does offer at least an approximation to the truth.

In random vibration the stresses vary in a manner which bears some resemblance to this last case, in that the peak stresses do occur at various levels, even though the various levels do not occur in a fixed sequence. We shall therefore accept the Miner criterion here, transferring it complete from its original context of sequences of stress cycles to the conditions of random vibration, making such modifications in its interpretation as become necessary in order to do so. In random vibration, in particular, we can no longer consider a number of cycles N_r at a stress of $\pm s_r$: we shall instead have to think of N_r as the number of peaks of level $+s_r$. And in random vibration the peaks do not occur at a finite number of levels: they are continuously distributed over the whole range of possible values, so we shall have to make provision for this.

It is clear that in applying our criterion of failure under random loading, in order to predict the probability of failure of a component during a given service life, we shall need to know the manner in which the peak values of the stress are distributed. We shall therefore consider in the next section the general problem of determining the peak distribution of a randomly varying quantity.

6.3 Peak Distribution of a Random Process

Suppose that we know the probability density $p(x)$ of a random process $\{x(t)\}$, not necessarily Gaussian, which we can assume represents the stress in a certain component. This tells us the probability that a member function $x(t)$ will at a given instant have a value within a certain range, or what amounts to the same thing, the proportion of its time which the member function $x(t)$ spends within a certain range of values; the proportion of time spent in the range $x_1 < x(t) < x_1 + dx$ is simply $p(x_1)\, dx$. But in considering mechanical failure, information as to *time spent* in a given range of values is of little relevance; in order to determine the probability of failure within a specified service life we must be able to determine the expected number of peaks occurring within a given range during a given time interval. We must now develop analysis which will enable us to do this. (See also Rice (reference 21).)

A peak value of $x(t)$ occurs whenever $x'(t) = 0$, provided that at the same time $x''(t)$ is negative: positive values of $x''(t)$ indicate either minima rather than maxima, or negative peaks which are not of interest. We may therefore express the probability of a peak occurring in the range $x_1 < x < x_1 + dx$ during time dt, as

$$\Pr[\text{Peak in } dx, dt] = \Pr \left[\left. \begin{array}{l} x_1 < x(t) < x_1 + dx \\ x'(t) = 0 \\ x''(t) < 0 \end{array} \right\} \text{ in time } dt \right]. \quad (1)$$

We are now concerned with the joint probability of three separate events, and so must treat the problem in accordance with the concepts of Section 2.7. The quantity on which analysis must be based is thus the joint probability density of $x(t)$, $x'(t)$, $x''(t)$, i.e. on

$$p(x, x', x''), \quad (2)$$

defined such that, at a given instant of time t_1,

$$p(x_1, x_1', x_1'')dx\, dx'\, dx'' = \Pr \left[\begin{array}{l} x_1 < x(t_1) < x_1 + dx \\ x_1' < x'(t_1) < x_1' + dx' \\ x_1'' < x''(t_1) < x_1'' + dx'' \end{array} \right] \quad (3)$$

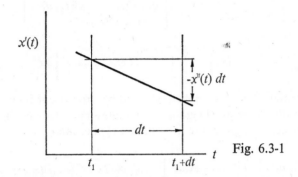

Fig. 6.3-1

If $x(t)$ is not known to be Gaussian both (1) and (2) can only be determined experimentally, and it is probably easier to determine (1) directly by experiment than to determine (2) experimentally and then to use it to calculate (1). But as we shall see in the next section, if $x(t)$ has a Gaussian distribution, the probability density represented by (2) can be expressed analytically in terms of the properties of $x(t)$. In such a case it will be useful to be able to express the probability defined by (1) in terms of the joint probability density (2). We shall now demonstrate how this can be done.

We want to express (1), which gives the probability of an event occurring during a given interval of time, in terms of (2), which gives the joint probability of certain occurrences at a given instant.

Consider the $x'(t)$, t curve in the interval $t_1 < t < t_1 + dt$ (Fig. 6.3-1). In the short interval dt the slope $x''(t)$ is effectively constant, so that the curve may be represented by a straight line of slope $x''(t_1)$: we are interested only in negative values of the quantity $x''(t)$. The value of $x'(t)$ becomes zero at some time during the interval dt only if this straight line intersects the t axis in the interval dt. This occurs only if

$$-x''(t_1)\,dt > x'(t_1) > 0, \qquad (4)$$

as can be seen from the diagram.

The probability of (1) is thus that of (3) integrated to include all negative values of x'', and, for each x'', all the values of x' covered by $x'(t_1)$ in (4). This gives

$$\text{Pr}\,[\text{Peak in } dx,\, dt] = \text{Pr} \begin{bmatrix} x_1 < x(t_1) < x_1 + dx \\ 0 < x'(t_1) < -x''(t_1)\, dt \\ -\infty < x''(t_1) < 0 \end{bmatrix}$$

$$= dx \int_{-\infty}^{0} \left[\int_{0}^{-x''\, dt} p(x, x', x'')\, dx' \right] dx''. \tag{5}$$

The integration with respect to dx' can be carried out immediately because the range of integration is infinitesimal. This having been done we can recognise that $x' = 0$, and (5) becomes

$$\text{Pr}\,[\text{Peak in } dx,\, dt] = -dx\, dt \int_{-\infty}^{0} x''\, p(x, x', x'')_{x'=0}\, dx''. \tag{6}$$

This gives us the probability of a peak occurring within the rectangle $dx\, dt$. If we integrate (6) over a given time interval, and over a given range of values of x we shall in the light of Section 2.6 obtain the expectation (or the average number expected on the basis of many trials over the same time interval), of peaks occurring within that range in that time interval.

Thus the expectation of peaks occurring in unit time in the range $x_A < x < x_B$ is given by

$$E_1\,[\text{peaks between } x_A \text{ and } x_B] =$$

$$-\int_{x_A}^{x_B} \left[\int_{-\infty}^{0} x''\, p(x, x', x'')_{x'=0}\, dx'' \right] dx \tag{7}$$

(using the symbol E_1 to indicate expectation per unit time).

From this result we find, for example, that the expectation per unit time of peaks with values greater than a certain value x_A is given by

$$E_1\,[\text{peaks} > x_A] = -\int_{x_A}^{\infty} \left[\int_{-\infty}^{0} x''\, p(x, x', x'')_{x'=0}\, dx'' \right] dx. \tag{8}$$

So if $p(x, x', x'')$ is known, the expectation per unit time of peaks exceeding any given limiting value can easily be obtained, and from this expectation the probability of the occurrence of such peaks within the intended service life of a component can be determined using the results of Section 2.6.

6.4 Peak Distribution of a Gaussian Random Process

The probability density of a three-dimensional Gaussian random process is given in Section 2.7 for variables $x(t)$, $y(t)$, $z(t)$. Adapting this result to our present needs by changing the variables to $x(t)$, $x'(t)$, $x''(t)$, and putting $x' = 0$, we obtain

$$p(x, x', x'')_{x'=0} =$$

$$\frac{1}{\sqrt{(8\pi^3 \det M)}} \exp\left[-\frac{M_{xx}x^2 + M_{x''x''}x''^2 + 2M_{xx''}xx''}{2\det M} \right], \quad (1)$$

where

$$\det M = \begin{vmatrix} \sigma_x^2 & \sigma_{xx'}^2 & \sigma_{xx''}^2 \\ \sigma_{xx'}^2 & \sigma_{x'}^2 & \sigma_{x'x''}^2 \\ \sigma_{xx''}^2 & \sigma_{x'x''}^2 & \sigma_{x''}^2 \end{vmatrix}, \quad (2)$$

and

$$\left. \begin{aligned} M_{xx} &= \sigma_{x'}^2 \sigma_{x''}^2 - \sigma_{x'x''}^4 \\ M_{x''x''} &= \sigma_x^2 \sigma_{x'}^2 - \sigma_{xx'}^4 \\ M_{xx''} &= \sigma_{xx'}^2 \sigma_{x'x''}^2 - \sigma_{x'}^2 \sigma_{xx''}^2 \end{aligned} \right\} \quad (3)$$

(Here $\sigma_x^2 = \langle x^2(t) \rangle$, $\sigma_{xx'}^2 = \langle x(t)x'(t) \rangle$, etc., as before.)

The expressions in (1), (2), and (3) can be greatly simplified if we express them in terms of the autocorrelation function and its derivatives.

Consider the autocorrelation function $R(\tau) = \langle x(t)\, x(t+\tau) \rangle$: differentiating successively with respect to τ we obtain

$$R'(\tau) = \langle x(t)\, x'(t+\tau) \rangle,$$
$$R''(\tau) = \langle x(t)\, x''(t+\tau) \rangle,$$
$$R'''(\tau) = \frac{\partial}{\partial \tau} \langle x(t)\, x''(t+\tau) \rangle$$
$$= \frac{\partial}{\partial \tau} \langle x(t-\tau)\, x''(t) \rangle$$
$$= -\langle x'(t-\tau)\, x''(t) \rangle.$$

So putting $\tau = 0$ and making use of the results of Section 3.7 we have

$$\left. \begin{aligned} \sigma_{xx'}^2 &= \langle x(t)\, x'(t) \rangle = R'(0) = 0, \\ \sigma_{xx''}^2 &= \langle x(t)\, x''(t) \rangle = R''(0), \\ \sigma_{x'x''}^2 &= \langle x'(t)\, x''(t) \rangle = -R'''(0) = 0. \end{aligned} \right\}$$

Also by Section 3.7

$$\left.\begin{array}{l}\sigma_x{}^2 = \langle x^2(t)\rangle = R(0),\\ \sigma_{x'}{}^2 = \langle x'^2(t)\rangle = -R''(0),\\ \sigma_{x''}{}^2 = \langle x''^2(t)\rangle = R''''(0).\end{array}\right\}$$

If we now write R, R'', R'''', to indicate $R(0)$, $R''(0)$, $R''''(0)$ – which will simplify the notation considerably – we can write (1), (2) and (3) in the form

$$p(x, x', x'')_{x'=0} =$$

$$\frac{1}{\sqrt{(8\pi^3 \det M)}} \exp\left[\frac{R'' R'''' x^2 - 2R''^2 xx'' + RR'' x''^2}{2 \det M}\right], \quad (4)$$

with $\det M = R''(R''^2 - RR'''')$.

The above expression (4) for $p(x, x', x'')$ can be inserted in 6.3(6) and gives, when the integration is carried out,

$$\Pr[\text{Peak in } dx, dt] = -dx\, dt \int_{-\infty}^{0} x''\, p(x, x', x'')_{x'=0}\, dx''$$

$$= \frac{-dx\, dt}{(2\pi)^{3/2} R R''} \left\{ \sqrt{(\det M)} \exp\frac{R'' R'''' x^2}{2 \det M} \right.$$

$$\left. +R''^2 x \sqrt{\left(\frac{\pi}{-2R R''}\right)} \left[1 + \text{erf}\frac{R''^2 x}{\sqrt{(-2R R'' \det M)}}\right] \exp\left(\frac{-x^2}{2R}\right) \right\}. \quad (5)$$

This simplifies considerably if we write

$$k^2 = \frac{R''^2}{(R R'''' - R''^2)} \; ; \quad \text{we then obtain}$$

$\Pr[\text{Peak in } dx, dt]$

$$= \frac{dx\, dt\, \sqrt{-R''}}{2\sqrt{2\pi R}} \frac{x}{\sqrt{(2R)}} \exp\left(-\frac{x^2}{2R}\right)$$

$$\left[1 + \text{erf}\frac{kx}{\sqrt{(2R)}} + \frac{1}{\sqrt{\pi}} \frac{\sqrt{(2R)}}{kx} \exp\left(-\frac{k^2 x^2}{2R}\right)\right]; \quad (6)$$

from this expression the expectation of peaks occurring in any time interval, within any range of x, can be determined by suitable integration.

Thus, for example, the expectation E_1 of peaks occurring in unit time which are greater than n times the root-mean-square value is given by

$$E_1 = \frac{1}{2\pi} \sqrt{\left(\frac{-R''}{R}\right)} \int_{n\sqrt{R}}^{\infty} \frac{x}{\sqrt{(2R)}} \exp\left(-\frac{x^2}{2R}\right)$$

$$\left[1 + \mathrm{erf}\,\frac{kx}{\sqrt{(2R)}} + \frac{1}{\sqrt{\pi}} \frac{\sqrt{(2R)}}{kx} \exp\left(-\frac{k^2 x^2}{2R}\right)\right] d\left(\frac{x}{\sqrt{(2R)}}\right). \qquad (7)$$

The value of the integral in (7) depends on the value of the integrand for all values of x within the range of integration: in cases of practical interest however the lower limit is normally large, so that only large values of $x/\sqrt{(2R)}$ have to be considered. Moreover in practice the quantity RR''''/R''^2 is close to unity, so that k is large also. This makes possible a considerable simplification, for with $kx/\sqrt{(2R)}$ large, $\exp(-k^2 x^2/2R)$ becomes negligible and $\mathrm{erf}\,kx/\sqrt{(2R)}$ tends to unity. We can therefore approximate to (6) by writing

$$\Pr\left[\text{Peak in } dx, dt\right] = \frac{dx\,dt\,\sqrt{(-R'')}}{\sqrt{2\pi R}} \frac{x}{\sqrt{(2R)}} \exp\left(-\frac{x^2}{2R}\right). \qquad (8)$$

Now integration is much simpler. The expectation of peaks in unit time which are greater than n times the RMS value is given by

$$E_1 = \frac{1}{\pi} \sqrt{\left(\frac{-R''}{R}\right)} \int_{n\sqrt{R}}^{\infty} \frac{x}{\sqrt{(2R)}} \exp\left(-\frac{x^2}{2R}\right) d\left(\frac{x}{\sqrt{(2R)}}\right)$$

$$= \frac{1}{\pi} \sqrt{\left(\frac{-R''}{R}\right)} \left[-\tfrac{1}{2} \exp\left(-\frac{x^2}{2R}\right)\right]_{n\sqrt{R}}^{\infty}$$

$$= \frac{1}{2\pi} \sqrt{\left(\frac{-R''}{R}\right)} \exp\left(-\frac{n^2}{2}\right). \qquad (9)$$

So to this degree of approximation the frequency of occurrence of peaks above a certain level depends on two factors: the quantity

$$\frac{1}{2\pi} \sqrt{\left(\frac{-R''}{R}\right)}$$

which is a characteristic of the random process, and the quantity

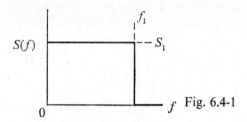

Fig. 6.4-1

$\exp(-n^2/2)$ which decreases rapidly as the level considered increases. We may write, using 3.7(7),

$$\frac{1}{2\pi}\sqrt{\left(\frac{-R''}{R}\right)} = \left[\frac{\int_0^\infty f^2\,S(f)\,df}{\int_0^\infty S(f)\,df}\right]^{\frac{1}{2}} :$$

this will have a large value if high frequencies predominate, and it is indeed under these conditions that we should expect many peaks to occur.

Let us consider as an example a randomly varying stress $s(t)$ which has a constant spectral density S_1 at all frequencies up to f_1, as shown in Fig. 6.4-1. We shall determine the expected number of peaks per unit time which exceed a given level s_A, assuming that $s(t)$ is Gaussian.

Using equation (9) we have

$$E_1 = \frac{1}{2\pi}\sqrt{\left(\frac{-R''}{R}\right)}\exp\left(-\frac{s_A{}^2}{2R}\right),$$

$$= \left[\frac{\int_0^{f_1} f^2\,S_1\,df}{\int_0^{f_1} S_1\,df}\right]^{\frac{1}{2}}\exp\left[-\frac{s_A{}^2}{2\int_0^{f_1} S_1\,df}\right]$$

$$= \frac{f_1}{\sqrt{3}}\exp\left(-\frac{s_A{}^2}{2\,S_1 f_1}\right).$$

The quantity $S_1 f_1$ in the exponent here is of course the mean-square value of $s(t)$.

If the limiting frequency f_1 in this case were 1000 cps., the expectation per second of peaks of magnitude greater than $5\sqrt{(S_1 f_1)}$ (i.e. greater than five times the root-mean-square value) would be

$$E_1 = \frac{1000}{\sqrt{3}} e^{-12\cdot 5} = 0\cdot 00215 \text{ per second:}$$

that is, the mean interval between such peaks would be 465 seconds, or about 8 minutes. The expectation of such a peak value occurring in any one minute would be $0\cdot 129$: the probability of the occurrence of such a value in any minute would, by 2.6(4), be $0\cdot 129 - \frac{1}{2}(0\cdot 129)^2 = 0\cdot 121$.

We may note that in this case the k^2 of equation (6) is $1\cdot 25$. With $x^2/2R = 12\cdot 5$, we have therefore,

$$\exp\left(-\frac{k^2 x^2}{2R}\right) = e^{-15\cdot 62} = 0\cdot 168 \times 10^{-6},$$

which is certainly negligible. Also

$$\text{erf } \frac{kx}{\sqrt{(2R)}} = \text{erf } 3\cdot 95 = 0\cdot 99999998;$$

our treating this as unity was certainly justified.

6.5 Peak Distribution and Failure

It might at first sight seem possible to design on the basis of calculating the probability of the occurrence of a stress peak greater than the ultimate strength of the material, assuming that such a stress would cause immediate failure. But such a peak might be of very brief duration and in consequence not cause failure. It seems reasonable to assume that in any case where such a stress occurred the combined effect of a sequence of lower stresses would cause greater damage. It is therefore on the probability of fatigue failure that we shall concentrate.

In order to apply the Miner criterion, 6.2(1), in the conditions of random loading, we still have to restate it in a form which is suitable for such application.

Suppose that a randomly varying stress $s(t)$, with mean value zero,

RV H

acts at a certain point in a structure for a time T. If we know the quantity $p_{pk}(s)$, such that

$$p_{pk}(s) \, ds \, dt = \Pr[\text{Peak in } ds, \, dt],$$

for all values of s, and if this is constant for all values of t, the expectation per unit time of peaks in the range $s_1 < s < s_1 + ds$ is simply

$$p_{pk}(s_1) \, ds,$$

and the expectation in time T is

$$T \, p_{pk}(s_1) \, ds. \tag{1}$$

Now the fatigue properties of the material can be determined and plotted as an $s - N$ curve, giving the number of cycles N of a stress with peak value s which the material will stand before failure. So using the Miner value for damage, we can say that, in time T, the expected damage due to peak stresses in the range $s_1 < s < s_1 + ds$ is

$$\frac{T \, p_{pk}(s_1) \, ds}{N(s_1)}, \tag{2}$$

where $N(s_1)$ is the number of cycles for failure under a stress with peak value s_1.

The expected total damage occurring during the time T under the random loading is the sum of all possible terms like this, and is given by the integral

$$T \int_0^\infty \frac{p_{pk}(s) \, ds}{N(s)}. \tag{3}$$

Failure will therefore occur, on the average, after a time $T = T_F$ such that damage is complete; that is, such that (3) is equal to unity. The Miner criterion for failure thus takes the form

$$T_F \int_0^\infty \frac{p_{pk}(s \, ds}{N(s)} = 1, \tag{4}$$

where T_F is the mean expected life. This can be written to give T_F directly as

$$T_F = \left[\int_0^\infty \frac{p_{pk}(s) \, ds}{N(s)} \right]^{-1}. \tag{5}$$

The expectation of failure during a service life T_S is given by

T_S/T_F, and if this is small, as in a practical case it must surely be, it will also give the probability of failure. So the probability of failure in a given service life is simply

$$\Pr[\text{Failure during } T_S] = T_S \int_0^\infty \frac{p_{pk}(s)\,ds}{N(s)}. \tag{6}$$

6.6 Envelope Fluctuation and Spectral Density Determination

A narrow-band filter offers an attractive method of determining the spectral density of any randomly varying quantity which can be obtained in electrical form. If the signal $x(t)$ is passed through an ideal band-pass filter of small bandwidth Δf and central frequency f_1, the mean-square value of the filtered signal is simply $S(f_1)\,\Delta f$, and the spectral density $S(f_1)$ at this frequency can be obtained from it simply by dividing by the bandwidth Δf. If this procedure is repeated over the whole range of frequencies the whole $S(f)$ curve can be established.

There are however practical difficulties which make the carrying out of this process less simple than it at first appears. Although it is possible to visualise a narrow-band filter which is ideal in the sense that it admits equally all frequencies within a certain small range and none outside this range, it is hardly possible to visualise a filter which is ideal in the sense that it has zero bandwidth. Because of the necessarily finite bandwidth the signal passed by a narrow-band filter is not a sinusoid: it is a randomly varying quantity whose form approximates to that of a modulated sine wave, of which the apparent carrier frequency is the central frequency of the filter, and whose amplitude fluctuates very much more slowly than the signal itself with a mean frequency dependent on the properties of the filter.

The nature of these amplitude fluctuations can be investigated theoretically by considering the envelope of the emergent signal, and analysis with this purpose is given by Rice in reference 21, (Paragraphs 3.7 and 3.8); we shall give no account of the analysis here, but simply quote the results. It is found that the envelope has a Rayleigh distribution with its probability density $p(x)$ given by

$$p(x) = \frac{x}{\sigma^2} e^{-x^2/\sigma^2}, \tag{1}$$

where σ^2 is the mean-square value of the filtered signal. (The similarity to 6.4(8) may be noted.) This implies a very considerable amplitude fluctuation, with the envelope spending nearly 30% of its time either below half or above twice the root-mean-square value of the filtered signal. Rice also investigates the peak distribution of the envelope and shows that peaks of the envelope – and so maximum amplitudes of the signal – occur with a mean frequency of $0 \cdot 641 \Delta f$, where Δf is the filter bandwidth. Thus for example a filter with a central frequency of 100 cps. and bandwidth 1 cps. would give a signal basically of frequency 100 cps., but with its amplitude fluctuating with a mean period of about $1 \cdot 5$ secs.

In determining spectral density, therefore, the mean-square value of the signal passed by the filter must be obtained by averaging over a period long enough to smooth out the effects of these amplitude fluctuations, and in order to ensure accuracy the length of record to be considered must always be chosen in accordance with the bandwidth of the filter used. If a filter is to be replaced by another of smaller bandwidth, with the object of giving the spectral density curve with greater detail, it will be necessary to process a greater length of signal in order to obtain equally reliable results. Consistency of spectral density measurements with a given duration of signal can always be improved by increasing filter bandwidth, but if this is done detail in the $S(f)$ curve may be lost.

It is possible to determine analytically the variance of spectral densities measured in this way, in terms of the filter characteristics and the length of record available. This is done for an ideal band-pass filter by Rice in reference 21, where it is shown that the variance σ^2 of a set of spectral densities $S_T(f)$ obtained for a given frequency using records of length T and a filter of bandwidth Δf is given by

$$\sigma^2 = \frac{S^2(f)}{T \Delta f},\qquad (2)$$

where $S(f)$ is the true spectral density.

Blackman and Tukey (reference 3) consider the same problem for a number of different filter characteristics and obtain results of the same order.

CHAPTER VII

SIMULATION OF RANDOM ENVIRONMENTS

7.1 Introduction

While it would be beyond the scope of this book to concern itself in any detail with the purely practical aspects of random vibration, it is nevertheless important that we should indicate how the basic concepts and the theory which we have developed are to be applied to practical problems. In the previous chapter we have seen how our theory can be applied to the basic problem of design: in this final chapter we shall consider the problem of environmental vibration testing, and show how a fundamental understanding of the theory of random vibration can contribute to the development of a technique which is of its nature almost entirely empirical.

7.2 Environmental Vibration Testing

Many equipments and components which are subjected to severe random loadings in service cannot well be tested in their actual service environments. A space-vehicle, for example, cannot be test-flown to ensure that it will stand up to powered flight, yet the effects may be disastrous if it fails to do so. And even where testing under service conditions is possible it may not be convenient or economic. There are in fact many good reasons for the development of testing techniques which aim to ensure, by means of tests in the factory, that an equipment will function satisfactorily when in service. This is the basic requirement of all environmental testing.

But the ways of fulfilling this requirement are various, and very different tests may be used according to the prevailing circumstances. In some cases it may be possible to tolerate a very large degree of overtest, and if this is so testing techniques can be relatively crude, and avoid any pretence of close simulation. In others it may be essential to avoid overtesting, but equally essential to avoid failure in service. It may be necessary to test a prototype whose service loadings cannot be known with any precision, or it may be necessary to test a batch of components whose service loadings are well established by measurements on a prototype in service. For our purposes here we shall assume that we are concerned with a refined testing technique, whose only possible basis is the close simulation of service conditions. There are obviously many factors other than the ability to withstand random vibration which can conveniently be assessed in an environmental test, but these do not concern us here.

It may be noted that exact simulation is not necessarily ideal in all circumstances, even if it is possible: the stressing which an equipment experiences under test is more likely to reduce subsequent fatigue life than to increase it.

If we accept then that close simulation is desirable, we have to consider how it is to be achieved. Exact reproduction during test of the actual service *loads* is very difficult, whether the loads arise from turbulence in the surrounding air or from the propulsion units. It is easier in practice to set out to reproduce the actual *motions* experienced in flight and particularly if a prototype has flown and has been sufficiently well provided with instrumentation, this is always theoretically possible. But even a test in which previously recorded motions are required to be reproduced is no simple matter. Complete simulation requires the matching of the motions of all points so that all have the correct spectra in all planes, and requires moreover that these motions be cross-correlated in exactly the same manner as in service. However, even if complete simulation is not possible, a good approximation to service conditions covered by a reasonable factor of overtest is naturally of considerable value. In most cases too, approximate methods of test can be vindicated by reference to actual performance in service.

We shall approach the problem of obtaining satisfactory simulation in two ways: we shall consider the implications of providing exact simulation of service motions at a finite number of points using as many vibrators as necessary, and we shall consider the results which can be achieved by using only a single vibrator and see to what extent the approximate simulation obtained can prove acceptable.

7.3 The General Problem of Simulation

Ideally an environmental test should provide motions exactly similar to those in service at all points of a body. But data and

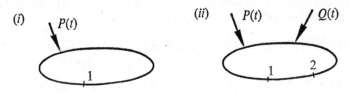

Fig. 7.3-1

monitoring facilities will only be available at a finite number of points, and we may accept that the basic problem of practical random vibration simulation is therefore to provide exact matching of the spectral densities of the motions at a number of points and of the cross spectral densities between them: this is in effect to impose prescribed spectral densities of motion at or between a prescribed number of points. For practical reasons we can assume that the number of points is finite; it will obviously be kept as small as possible consistent with precision. The number of vibrators which need to be used for exact simulation will depend on the number of points at which the exact simulation is required. We shall consider this basic problem for progressively more ambitious approaches to complete simulation.

To impose a prescribed spectral density at a single point is clearly possible with a single force, wherever applied, provided that the spectral density of the force can be controlled. Denoting the applied randomly varying force by $P(t)$, and its spectral density by $S_P(f)$, the motion in a given direction of the prescribed point 1 (Fig. 7.3-1(i)) will have spectral density $S_1(f)$ defined by

$$S_1(f) = |\alpha_{1P}|^2 S_P(f), \tag{1}$$

where α_{1P} is the receptance giving the response due to a harmonically varying force. Suitable shaping of $S_P(f)$ will obviously give $S_1(f)$ any desired form.

To impose prescribed spectral densities at two points and a prescribed cross spectral density between them is a little more complicated and it cannot, in general, be achieved with fewer than two vibrators suitably excited. Consider the system shown in Fig. 7.3-1(ii). If the two applied forces $P(t)$, $Q(t)$ have spectral densities $S_P(f)$, $S_Q(f)$, and cross spectral density $S_{PQ}(f)$, then the spectral densities $S_1(f)$, $S_2(f)$ and the cross spectral densities $S_{12}(f)$, $S_{21}(f)$ of the motions of the points 1, 2 are given by

$$\left.\begin{aligned}
S_1(f) &= \alpha_{1P}^* \alpha_{1P} S_P(f) + \alpha_{1P}^* \alpha_{1Q} S_{PQ}(f) + \alpha_{1Q}^* \alpha_{1P} S_{QP}(f) \\
&\qquad + \alpha_{1Q}^* \alpha_{1Q} S_Q(f) \\
S_2(f) &= \alpha_{2P}^* \alpha_{2P} S_P(f) + \alpha_{2P}^* \alpha_{2Q} S_{PQ}(f) + \alpha_{2Q}^* \alpha_{2P} S_{QP}(f) \\
&\qquad + \alpha_{2Q}^* \alpha_{2Q} S_Q(f) \\
S_{12}(f) &= \alpha_{1P}^* \alpha_{2P} S_P(f) + \alpha_{1P}^* \alpha_{2Q} S_{PQ}(f) + \alpha_{1Q}^* \alpha_{2P} S_{QP}(f) \\
&\qquad + \alpha_{1Q}^* \alpha_{2Q} S_Q(f) \\
S_{21}(f) &= \alpha_{2P}^* \alpha_{1P} S_P(f) + \alpha_{2P}^* \alpha_{1Q} S_{PQ}(f) + \alpha_{2Q}^* \alpha_{1P} S_{QP}(f) \\
&\qquad + \alpha_{2Q}^* \alpha_{1Q} S_Q(f)
\end{aligned}\right\} \quad (2)$$

To specify a cross spectral density involves specification of two quantities – its real and imaginary parts: on the other hand as, say, $S_{PQ}(f)$ is the complex conjugate of $S_{QP}(f)$ only two quantities are needed to specify the pair of cross spectral densities. We see therefore from equations (2), that in order that the four quantities $S_1(f)$, $S_2(f)$ and the real and imaginary parts of $S_{12}(f)$ may be given a set of prescribed values, it is necessary that all four adjustable quantities – $S_P(f)$, $S_Q(f)$, and the real and imaginary parts of $S_{PQ}(f)$ – be at our disposal. Extension of this argument shows that exact simulation of the spectral densities at and between three points will require the matching of nine quantities and so in general will require the use and complete control of at least three vibrators. The minimum number of vibrators required is in fact always equal to the number of points at which exact matching is required.

But in hoping to obtain exact simulation at a number of points we are not necessarily approaching the problem in the best way. We shall see in the next section that in certain circumstances a satisfactory though approximate degree of simulation may be possible with very few vibrators, or even with only one.

7.4 Simulation with Limited Means

In considering how to simulate service motions exactly by means of a hypothetical test, it is easy to assume that adequate records of the service motion are available to us. But such complete information is not easily obtained and in practice the data available may be very limited indeed: in such cases a degree of simulation is possible, but it cannot be complete. It may happen for example that

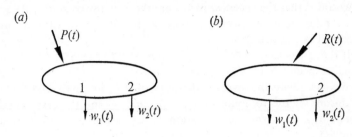

Fig. 7.4-1

we have information only about the spectral densities at a few points, and no information at all about cross-correlations. A consideration of such a limited degree of simulation is therefore relevant.

In specifying an environmental test it is naturally desirable to use a minimum of experimental equipment and of service data. If it is possible to obtain adequate simulation by using a single vibrator and a single accelerometer a more refined test will be unjustified. Let us investigate therefore whether it is possible to provide any sort of simulation with a single vibrator and a single accelerometer. We shall approach this problem by postulating a given service loading: we shall design a test in which a single vibrator arbitrarily placed is adjusted to reproduce the service motion at a single point only: we shall then compare the motions in service and test at one other representative point, and the cross-correlations in service and test of the motions at two points. We shall do this first for a simple service loading and then repeat the analysis for a more general loading.

Let us assume first that the service loading on a component consists of a randomly varying force $P(t)$, as in Fig. 7.4-1(a), which has spectral density $S_P(f)$. We shall denote the motions of the points 1, 2, etc. in given directions by $w_1(t)$, $w_2(t)$, etc., and their spectral densities by $S_1(f)$, $S_2(f)$, etc. We shall distinguish quantities pertaining to this case – that is, to the service conditions – by adding the superscript (a), so that, for example, the spectral density of the motion at the point 2 in service is written as $S_2^{(a)}(f)$.

Let the force applied during test be denoted by $R(t)$, and suppose it to act at some arbitrarily chosen point as in Fig. 7.4-1(b): let it have spectral density $S_R(f)$. Quantities occurring in this case – that is, during the test – will be distinguished by the superscript (b). It is assumed that the specified forces are the only forces acting in each case, other than constraint forces, and that the constraints are identical in the two cases.

If the test is to give perfect simulation $S_1^{(b)}(f)$ and $S_2^{(b)}(f)$ must be equal respectively to $S_1^{(a)}(f)$ and $S_2^{(a)}(f)$.

We can relate the spectral densities of displacements and forces by means of the receptances α_{1P}, α_{2P}, etc., (giving the response at points 1, 2 to harmonic excitation in the sense of $P(t)$, $R(t)$) as follows:

$$\left.\begin{aligned} S_1^{(a)}(f) &= |\alpha_{1P}|^2 \, S_P(f) \\ S_2^{(a)}(f) &= |\alpha_{2P}|^2 \, S_P(f) \end{aligned}\right\} \tag{1}$$

in service,

and

$$\left.\begin{aligned} S_1^{(b)}(f) &= |\alpha_{1R}|^2 \, S_R(f) \\ S_2^{(b)}(f) &= |\alpha_{2R}|^2 \, S_R(f) \end{aligned}\right\} \tag{2}$$

during test.

There is no reason why these pairs of quantities should be equal unless we do something to make them so; $S_P(f)$ is of course a fixed quantity and the α's are fixed parameters for the component, but we have control over the spectrum of $S_R(f)$ and can at least adjust this to ensure that $S_1^{(a)}(f) = S_1^{(b)}(f)$. To do this requires that the spectrum of the force $R(t)$ be shaped such that

$$S_R(f) = \frac{|\alpha_{1P}|^2}{|\alpha_{1R}|^2} \, S_P(f). \tag{3}$$

If we adjust $S_R(f)$ so that (3) is satisfied, we shall have obtained exact simulation of the motion at the point 1, but we must accept whatever motion arises at the point 2. The spectral density of this motion is now given by

$$S_2^{(b)}(f) = |\alpha_{2R}|^2 \times \frac{|\alpha_{1P}|^2}{|\alpha_{1R}|^2} \, S_P(f),$$

$$= \frac{|\alpha_{2R}|^2}{|\alpha_{2P}|^2} \frac{|\alpha_{1P}|^2}{|\alpha_{1R}|^2} \, S_2^{(a)}(f). \tag{4}$$

So the spectral densities of the motions at the point 2 will only be identical if

$$\frac{|\alpha_{2R}|^2 |\alpha_{1P}|^2}{|\alpha_{2P}|^2 |\alpha_{1R}|^2} = 1, \tag{5}$$

and there is, in general, no reason why this should be true.

It is interesting to apply these results to a beam, for which the receptances are already known. Using our usual notation, the displacements $w_1(t)$, $w_2(t)$ now become the displacements $w(x_1, t)$, $w(x_2, t)$ at x_1, x_2 respectively: we can assume that in (*a*) the force $P(t)$ is applied at x_P, and that in (*b*) the force $R(t)$ is applied at x_R. Then, using the results of Section 4.6, the receptances are given by

$$|\alpha_{1P}|^2 = \left(\sum_r \mu_r X_r\right)^2 + \left(\sum_r \mu_r Y_r\right)^2 \tag{6}$$

$$\text{where } \mu_r = \frac{w_r(x_1)\, w_r(x_P)}{M_r},$$

$$\left.\begin{aligned} X_r &= \frac{f_r^2 - f^2}{4\pi^2[(f_r^2 - f^2)^2 + \eta_r^2 f_r^4]}, \\[2mm] Y_r &= \frac{\eta_r f_r^2}{4\pi^2[(f_r^2 - f^2)^2 + \eta_r^2 f_r^4]}, \end{aligned}\right\} \tag{7}$$

with similar expressions for the remaining receptances.

There is nothing here to encourage us to hope that (5) might be satisfied, and this confirms the conclusion of the previous section that a simple environmental test of this type cannot provide complete simulation.

But we have seen that when damping is small and peaks well separated we can replace (6) approximately by

$$|\alpha_{1P}|^2 = \sum_r \frac{\mu_r^2}{16\pi^4[(f_r^2 - f^2)^2 + \eta_r^2 f_r^4]}, \tag{8}$$

where only one term need be considered near to any one natural frequency, and where μ_r again has the form shown in (7). We now have

$$\frac{|\alpha_{2R}|^2 |\alpha_{1P}|^2}{|\alpha_{1R}|^2 |\alpha_{2P}|^2} = \frac{[w_r(x_2)\, w_r(x_R)]^2}{[w_r(x_1)\, w_r(x_R)]^2} \times \frac{[w_r(x_1)\, w_r(x_P)]^2}{[w_r(x_2)\, w_r(x_P)]^2} = 1.$$

We thus conclude that under these conditions of small damping and well separated peaks equation (5) is satisfied, nearly enough, so that the motion of the point 2 – and by similar reasoning that of every other point on the body – is correctly simulated. We may presume that even when these conditions are not strictly satisfied simulation will be approximately correct.

Similar analysis to the above can be carried out to compare the cross spectral densities of the motions of two points 2 and 3 during the service loading (a) and the test ioading (b). Denoting this cross spectral density by $S_{23}(f)$ we have from Section 5.4

$$
\left.
\begin{aligned}
S_{23}^{(a)}(f) &= \alpha_{2P}{}^* \, \alpha_{3P} \, S_P(f), \\
S_{23}^{(b)}(f) &= \alpha_{2R}{}^* \, \alpha_{3R} \, S_R(f).
\end{aligned}
\right\}
\tag{9}
$$

If $S_R(f)$ is now adjusted as in (3), we find from (9) that

$$
\frac{S_{23}^{(b)}(f)}{S_{23}^{(a)}(f)} = \frac{\alpha_{2R}{}^* \, \alpha_{3R}}{\alpha_{2P}{}^* \, \alpha_{3P}} \times \frac{|\alpha_{1P}|^2}{|\alpha_{1R}|^2}.
\tag{10}
$$

Again this is not in general unity, but it will be so for low damping if we use our approximate beam receptances with

$$
\alpha_{1P} = \sum_r \mu_r (X_r - i Y_r), \text{ etc.}
\tag{11}
$$

At least for low dampings, a test using a single vibrator with a properly shaped spectrum has thus proved capable of giving good simulation not only of direct spectra but also of the cross spectra of the motions.

Similar results can be obtained in the same way if the service loading is assumed to consist of distributed pressures acting over the surface of the body, whatever cross-correlations exist (provided that these have stationary properties). It will be convenient again to consider the body to be a beam. Let us consider in case (a) a service loading which consists of a pressure of intensity $p(x, t)$ acting over the length of the beam from $x = 0$ to $x = l$, such that the cross spectral density of the intensities at any two points x_A, x_B is given by $S_p(x_A, x_B; f)$. Let us see how closely the resulting motions can be simulated by a test, case (b), in which the beam is loaded by a single force $R(t)$ acting at $x = x_R$, with spectral density $S_R(f)$. These loadings are indicated in Fig. 7.4-2.

It is again assumed that the specified loadings are the only applied forces and that constraints are identical in the two cases.

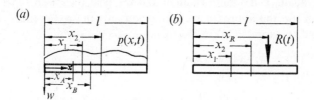

Fig. 7.4-2

The motions of points x_1 and x_2 in the two cases have spectral densities given respectively by

$$S_1^{(a)}(f) = \int_0^l \int_0^l \alpha_{1A}^* \, \alpha_{1B} \, S_p(x_A, x_B; f) \, dx_A \, dx_B$$

$$S_2^{(a)}(f) = \int_0^l \int_0^l \alpha_{2A}^* \, \alpha_{2B} \, S_p(x_A, x_B; f) \, dx_A \, dx_B$$

$$\left.\vphantom{\int}\right\} \quad (12)$$

in service,

and

$$S_1^{(b)}(f) = |\alpha_{1R}|^2 \, S_R(f)$$

$$S_2^{(b)}(f) = |\alpha_{2R}|^2 \, S_R(f)$$

$$\left.\vphantom{\int}\right\} \quad (13)$$

during test.

We can again adjust $S_R(f)$ so that the motion of x_1 has the same spectral density in the test as in service: if this is done

$$|\alpha_{1R}|^2 \, S_R(f) = \int_0^l \int_0^l \alpha_{1A}^* \, \alpha_{1B} \, S_p(x_A, x_B; f) \, dx_A \, dx_B, \qquad (14)$$

so that in the test

$$S_2^{(b)}(f) = \frac{|\alpha_{2R}|^2}{|\alpha_{1R}|^2} \times \int_0^l \int_0^l \alpha_{1A}^* \, \alpha_{1B} \, S_p(x_A, x_B; f) \, dx_A \, dx_B,$$

and the ratio between the test and service spectral densities at x_2 is given by

$$\frac{S_2^{(b)}(f)}{S_2^{(a)}(f)} = \frac{|\alpha_{2R}|^2}{|\alpha_{1R}|^2} \times \frac{\displaystyle\int_0^l \int_0^l \alpha_{1A}^* \, \alpha_{1B} \, S_p(x_A, x_B; f) \, dx_A \, dx_B}{\displaystyle\int_0^l \int_0^l \alpha_{2A}^* \, \alpha_{2B} \, S_p(x_A, x_B; f) \, dx_A \, dx_B}. \qquad (15)$$

This will clearly not, in general, be unity.

But again, if damping is small and the peaks are well separated, we can use the approximate expressions for the receptances, as in (8), and so express (15) in the form

$$\frac{S_2^{(b)}(f)}{S_2^{(a)}(f)} = \frac{w_r^2(x_2)\, w_r^2(x_R)}{w_r^2(x_1)\, w_r^2(x_R)}$$

$$\times \frac{w_r^2(x_1) \displaystyle\int_0^l \int_0^l w_r(x_A)\, w_r(x_B)\, S_p(x_A, x_B; f)\, dx_A\, dx_B}{w_r^2(x_2) \displaystyle\int_0^l \int_0^l w_r(x_A)\, w_r(x_B)\, S_p(x_A, x_B; f)\, dx_A\, dx_B} = 1.$$

Under these circumstances then, the motions during test at all points of the body have the correct spectral densities.

Similarly the cross spectral densities of the motions at two points x_2 and x_3 in the two cases are given by

$$\left. \begin{aligned} S_{23}^{(a)}(f) &= \int_0^l \int_0^l \alpha_{2A}{}^* \alpha_{3B}\, S_p(x_A, x_B; f)\, dx_A\, dx_B, \\ &\qquad\qquad\qquad \text{in service,} \\ S_{23}^{(b)}(f) &= \alpha_{2R}{}^* \alpha_{3R}\, S_R(f), \quad \text{in test.} \end{aligned} \right\} \tag{16}$$

If $S_R(f)$ is adjusted as in (14), the ratio of the two cross spectral densities is

$$\frac{S_{23}^{(b)}(f)}{S_{23}^{(a)}(f)} = \frac{\alpha_{2R}{}^* \alpha_{3R}}{\alpha_{1R}{}^* \alpha_{1R}} \times \frac{\displaystyle\int_0^l \int_0^l \alpha_{1A}{}^* \alpha_{1B}\, S_p(x_A, x_B; f)\, dx_A\, dx_B}{\displaystyle\int_0^l \int_0^l \alpha_{2A}{}^* \alpha_{3B}\, S_p(x_A, x_B; f)\, dx_A\, dx_B}. \tag{17}$$

For small damping and well separated peaks this also becomes unity, and again the test gives complete simulation of the service motions.

In that many equipments and components in which random vibration is troublesome in practice are lightly damped, these results can be considered very encouraging: it does seem likely that acceptable simulation of service random vibration environments can be achieved in a test using very simple equipment and based on very limited data. But the results should not be taken too literally as proving that a single vibrator used to match spectral densities at a single point is necessarily adequate in all circumstances, even when damping is small. The arrangements for spectral shaping necessary to ensure that $S_R(f)$ satisfies (14) and so to give the correct spectral density at the point x_1 will necessarily fall short of mathematical perfection. No physical vibrator could, for example, excite a mode for which its point of application was a node, or a mode which had no component in the direction of the force, and any mode with a node at x_1 would necessarily remain undetected and so unsimulated. The best arrangements for testing equipment must depend on its particular characteristics, and are best established by experiment guided by analysis of this sort.

Where the low-damping approximation is not permissible, a satisfactory degree of simulation can only be achieved by using a number of vibrators. But although with a number of vibrators closer simulation is attainable, it does not follow that it can be easily attained. With two spectral densities and one cross spectral density under the control of the operator, spectrum adjustment over the whole frequency range is not easy: when there are more than two vibrators the difficulty is greatly increased.

7.5 Further Problems of Environmental Testing

Without trespassing on practical detail, which we are intending to avoid here, we can discuss in a general way two subsidiary problems which may arise in practical environmental testing. These are, firstly, the problem of testing separately a part of a whole equipment, and secondly the problem of providing a test suitable for a sequence of nominally identical equipments which have nevertheless slight differences in their response characteristics.

The Separate Testing of Subcomponents. In the previous section we have seen that the simulation of the random motions experienced by a body in service may under certain circumstances be much easier than might have been expected on the basis of the general arguments of Section 7.3. Good results were seen to be possible even with a single vibrator when circumstances were favourable; that is, with low damping, well separated natural frequencies, and advantageously sited vibrator and measuring devices. The arguments used to reach this conclusion were applicable only to complete equipments; they cannot be applied to a separated part of an equipment unless its service constraint conditions can be accurately reproduced during the test. The physical reasons for this are not difficult to see.

In general the motion of a body, given by

$$w(x, t) = \sum_r w_r(x)\, \xi_r(t),$$

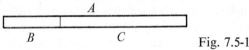

Fig. 7.5-1

(using the result for a beam, for convenience) contains contributions from all the normal modes $w_r(x)$, whose magnitudes are given at any instant by the values of the corresponding normal coordinates $\xi_r(t)$. The $\xi_r(t)$ have spectral densities $S_{\xi_r}(f)$ – and in general cross spectral densities $S_{\xi_r \xi_s}(f)$ too – extending over a wide range of frequencies. But when damping is low so that response peaks are high the $S_{\xi_r}(f)$ are each effectively restricted to a narrow range of frequencies about their corresponding natural frequency. In such a case, therefore, the motion $w(x, t)$ is made up essentially of a number of normal-mode motions, with each mode participating effectively only at its own natural frequency. And this happens, irrespective of the positioning of the exciting loads, within limits, whether a body is in service or is being tested. We benefit here from a body's enthusiasm for vibrating in its own normal modes at its own natural frequencies, which it displays equally well in service and under test.

It must be obvious that if we remove a part of the equipment and attempt to test it on its own, as we might very reasonably wish to do, we shall not be assisted in this way.

Let us consider for simplicity a beam A, consisting of two separable parts, B and C, as indicated in Fig. 7.5-1. Suppose that we wish to test section B separately; then we must ensure that the motion of B under test is substantially that experienced in service as a part of A. The service spectrum of the motion of any point on A – and so of any point on B – will be heavily coloured by the natural frequencies of A: the spectral densities will have high values near the natural frequencies of A and low values elsewhere. (We assume that the damping is light, but similar effects will be found to some degree in any system.) And we must provide a test in which each point of B reproduces this behaviour.

It must be clear immediately that this will not be easy. B is easy to excite in its own normal modes and at its own natural frequencies but these are not likely to coincide with those of A. This difficulty can be overcome to some extent by providing excitation through a vibrator with its force spectrum very severely shaped in order that the motion of some given point should have the correct spectrum. In this case the total applied force may need to be very large in order to excite B at frequencies where its receptance is low. But also in this case we cannot expect good simulation at more than one point because although we have excited the correct *frequencies* we have not excited the correct *modes*. When A vibrates as a whole, substantially correct motions are imposed on B by the forces applied by C at the junction, which effectively restrict its motion to the normal modes of A: if B is to be tested separately we must expect to have to apply the equivalent of such forces, correctly correlated, artificially.

So in testing a subcomponent in isolation we must pay very much greater attention to matching the motions and relative motions of different points, and we must expect to use more vibrators in order to do this successfully. There are clearly advantages in testing large subcomponents with the remainder of the equipment attached.

The Problem of Inconsistencies. In an ideal environmental vibration test we should arrange to excite in the equipment under test the actual motions which it would later experience in service. But as the test of any particular equipment must in practice precede its service motions, we must content ourselves by aiming to simulate motions which have already been experienced in service by another equipment having nominally identical service conditions and response characteristics.

The difficulty here is not so much that there are differences in the environments of successive equipments, although these must be expected to exist and be covered by a suitable factor of safety. The main difficulty is that although the motions of successive equipments will give spectra which are generally similar, showing similar, and similarly spaced, peaks characteristic of the frequency response of the equipments, only slight discrepancies between the frequencies at which these peaks occur will be necessary to cause serious simulation difficulties.

Suppose that two nominally similar equipments, A_1 and A_2, under service conditions, give spectra of which corresponding peaks occur at slightly different frequencies f_1 and f_2. If we were to use a spectrum taken from A_1 as a basis for an environmental test, we should find ourselves attempting to test A_2 by exciting in it motions giving rise to a spectrum with a peak at f_1. This would be difficult to do because A_2 would respond well only at f_2. It would also be quite useless as a test because the correct test for A_2 would require to give a peak at f_2, where there would be a peak in service.

This gives a sense of proportion to any ambition we might have for achieving 'exact' simulation. To overcome this difficulty, tests must either incorporate a great deal of overtest and arrange to excite spectra which everywhere exceed any possible service spectra, or they must incorporate sufficient flexibility to accept peaks at frequencies differing only slightly from those obtained in service, if these should prove easy to excite. The latter procedure is effectively used when spectra are measured, in service and under test, using broad-band filters, of $\frac{1}{3}$-octave, say: some detail is lost but these troublesome discrepancies are lost too. It may also be possible to develop an environmental test in which loads, rather than motions are simulated, but there are many practical difficulties involved in determining the service loadings. A composite technique in which a suitable test loading is inferred analytically from the motions of a prototype, this loading being applied to all subsequent units, may offer a solution.

APPENDIX

GENERAL THEORY OF VIBRATION

A.1 Introduction

It can presumably be assumed that those who are concerned with random vibration already have some knowledge of vibration theory. But it cannot necessarily be assumed that this knowledge is very extensive. Many engineers are in fact insufficiently familiar with normal-mode theory to be able to use it effectively to determine the motions under periodic or transient excitation of a complex structure such as an aircraft. As many of the applications of random vibration theory do concern complicated structures, a knowledge of normal-mode analysis is of great assistance in this subject, and it has seemed worth-while to give some account of it here. It has been thought best, however, to confine this account within an appendix in order not to interfere with the exposition of the theory of random vibration. As the purpose of normal-mode theory is to make applicable to a complex system the results obtained for a single-degree-of-freedom system, these results must first be established. Lagrange's equations will then be introduced, making possible the development of the general theory of vibrating systems.

A.2 The Simple Spring-Mass System

Consider the simple system shown in Fig. A.2-1 in which a mass m is supported by a spring of stiffness k, and is subjected to a harmonically varying force $P_0 \cos \omega t$. It will be assumed that damping is viscous and such as to exert a force $-c\dot{x}$, where x is the displacement of the mass.

The equation of motion of the system is then

$$m\ddot{x} + c\dot{x} + kx = P_0 \cos \omega t, \tag{1}$$

or, writing $c/m = 2\Delta$, and $k/m = p^2$,

$$\ddot{x} + 2\Delta\dot{x} + p^2 x = \frac{P_0}{m} \cos \omega t. \tag{2}$$

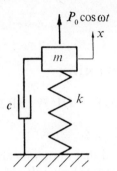

Fig. A.2-1

The solution of (2) consists of two parts: a complementary function obtained by solving with the right-hand side equal to zero (which itself gives the behaviour in free vibration), and a particular integral depending on the actual right-hand side.

The complementary function is obtained by substituting $x = C\,e^{\lambda t}$ in

$$x + 2\Delta\dot{x} + p^2 x = 0,$$

leading to an auxiliary equation which is a quadratic in λ,

$$\lambda^2 + 2\Delta\lambda + p^2 = 0:$$

solution of this equation in the usual way gives

$$\lambda = -\Delta \pm i\sqrt{(p^2 - \Delta^2)},$$

implying that

$$x = A\,e^{-\Delta t}\sin(p't + \varepsilon), \qquad (3)$$

where A and ε are constants, and $p' = \sqrt{(p^2 - \Delta^2)}$.

The complementary function (3) thus represents a damped oscillation and is only a transient phenomenon.

The particular integral of (2) is most easily obtained by solving, not (2), but the equation

$$\ddot{x} + 2\Delta\dot{x} + p^2 x = \frac{P_0}{m}\,e^{i\omega t}. \qquad (4)$$

As $e^{i\omega t} = \cos\omega t + i\sin\omega t$, the solution of (4) will combine the displacement due to the real force $P_0\cos\omega t$ and that due to an imaginary force $iP_0 \sin \omega t$. The superfluous terms in the solution will be imaginary and clearly labelled by the presence in each of them of the quantity i, so the real part of the solution of (4) gives the solution of (2).

Substituting $x = x_0 e^{i\omega t}$ in (4), we obtain

$$-\omega^2 x_0 + i2\Delta\omega x_0 + p^2 x_0 = P_0/m,$$

$$\text{or } x_0 = \frac{P_0}{m(p^2 - \omega^2 + i2\Delta\omega)}. \tag{5}$$

Equation (5) can also be written as

$$x_0 = \frac{P_0 e^{-i\phi}}{m\sqrt{[(p^2 - \omega^2)^2 + 4\Delta^2\omega^2]}}, \tag{6}$$

$$\text{where } \tan \phi = 2\Delta\omega/(p^2 - \omega^2),$$

and so the particular integral of (4) is

$$x = x_0 e^{i\omega t} = \frac{P_0 e^{i(\omega t - \phi)}}{m\sqrt{[(p^2 - \omega^2)^2 + 4\Delta^2\omega^2]}}. \tag{7}$$

The particular integral of (2) – the motion in forced vibration after the transient has vanished – is thus the real part of (7), that is

$$x = \frac{P_0 \cos(\omega t - \phi)}{m\sqrt{[(p^2 - \omega^2)^2 + 4\Delta^2\omega^2]}}. \tag{8}$$

The complete solution of equation (2) is then the sum of equations (3) and (8), with the constants chosen to satisfy the initial conditions.

Before leaving this system it is important to note that the solution (8) for steady-state harmonic response is obtainable immediately from (5) by plotting on the Argand diagram as in Fig. A.2-2. The phasors – loosely, vectors – representing $P_0 e^{i\omega t}$ and $x_0 e^{i\omega t}$ must have the phase difference and modulus ratio of the actual motion as given by (8). Plotting of P_0 and x_0 is sufficient to show these, and so the whole behaviour in response to harmonic excitation is given by the complex ratio x_0/P_0, which we term the complex receptance – or simply, *receptance* – and denote by $\alpha(i\omega)$. For the present system therefore, from (5),

$$\alpha(i\omega) = \frac{1}{m(p^2 - \omega^2 + i2\Delta\omega)}. \tag{9}$$

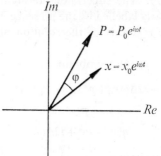

Fig. A.2-2

In the above discussion we have assumed that damping is viscous, but in many physical systems a model which more nearly reproduces hysteretic behaviour seems more applicable. In harmonic or near-harmonic motions such behaviour can be simulated by assuming that in equation (1) $c = C/\omega$ (where C is constant), or that in equation (4) the spring term is complex and equal to $p^2(1+i\eta)$. In this case the solution corresponding to (5) is

$$x_0 = \frac{P_0}{m(p^2-\omega^2+i\eta p^2)}$$

and the receptance is given by

$$\alpha(i\omega) = \frac{1}{m(p^2-\omega^2+i\eta p^2)}. \tag{10}$$

It is often desirable to have a non-dimensional description of the degree of damping existing in a system. When the damping is viscous the ratio of the existing damping to critical damping gives a convenient parameter, but this ratio is hardly applicable to hysteretic damping for which critical damping is not readily defined. Because of this it is convenient to make use of the quantity Q: this is a quantity more commonly associated with electrical circuit analysis, but where low damping permits certain approximations it proves even more readily applicable to vibrating systems.

We shall define Q for a single-degree-of-freedom system with small damping as the magnification factor at resonance; that is, the ratio of amplitude at the resonance frequency to that at zero fre-

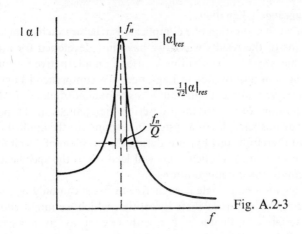

Fig. A.2-3

quency. Neglecting certain small terms on the assumption that damping is small we obtain for viscous damping, from (9),

$$Q = \left| \frac{\alpha(i\omega_n)}{\alpha(i0)} \right| = \frac{p^2}{2\Delta\omega_n}, \text{ where } \omega_n(=p) \text{ is the natural frequency,}$$

$$= \frac{\sqrt{(km)}}{c}, \tag{11}$$

and for hysteretic damping, from (10),

$$Q = \left| \frac{\alpha(i\omega_n)}{\alpha(i0)} \right| = \frac{p^2}{\eta p^2},$$

$$= \frac{1}{\eta}. \tag{12}$$

It can also be shown that, to the same degree of approximation (assuming small damping), the width of the frequency response characteristic, taken at a level of $1/\sqrt{2}$ of the resonance amplitude, is in both cases f_n/Q where f_n is the resonance frequency. (See Fig. A.2-3.) This fact enables us to determine Q whenever the corresponding receptance at zero frequency is not readily obtained: this is normally so when we consider the behaviour of more complicated systems.

A.3 Lagrange's Equations

To treat the vibration of a complicated structure such as an aircraft by means of the results which we have just developed for a simple spring-mass system, we shall make use of an alternative formulation of the laws of motion due to Lagrange. To comprehend Lagrange's equations we must generalise our ideas about coordinates and forces. Any equations of motion must describe the changes in the position of the various particles of a system in response to the applied forces: we shall therefore start by considering the problem of specifying the position of a single particle: this will lead on to the specification of more complicated configurations.

The position of a single particle free in space can only be specified completely by means of three quantities, which we might choose as its cartesian coordinates x, y, z with respect to given axes. But clearly there are infinitely many other ways in which the position of the particle can be specified: we could use polar coordinates, for example, or the distances from three fixed points, or the lengths of perpendiculars dropped on to three given surfaces. We may reasonably regard any of these sets of quantities as a complete set of coordinates. Whichever set we choose, three quantities will be necessary, and we say that such a particle has three degrees of freedom. Any other set of coordinates is determinable when the coordinates of one set are known.

These three degrees of freedom may be reduced by the presence of *constraints*, which are essentially restrictions imposing geometrical relationships between the coordinates of the set: if three coordinates of a single particle are given, and a constraint exists, they cannot be independent. If for example a particle can only move on the plane $x = 2y$ it has only two degrees of freedom, for if y is stated x can be determined. If a particle is restricted to the line $x = 2y$, $y = 2z$ it has only one degree of freedom, for a knowledge of z is sufficient to define the position completely. As each constraint implies the existence of one additional relationship between coordinates, it follows that the number of degrees of freedom is equal to the total possible number of degrees of freedom less the number of constraints. The number of degrees of freedom is always equal to the number of independent coordinates necessary to define position.

Two particles have potentially six degrees of freedom – three for each: their positions can be defined by six coordinates, which could be their cartesian coordinates $x_1, y_1, z_1, x_2, y_2, z_2$. The number of degrees of freedom and so the number of independent coordinates may be reduced by constraints on each particle of the type considered above. A pair of particles, moreover, may be subject to constraints restricting their relative motion: this would be the case if, for example, the particles were connected so that the distance between them remained constant. This latter condition could be expressed in the form $(x_2 - x_1)^2 + (y_2 - y_1)^2 + (z_2 - z_1)^2 = c^2$, and again the constraint condition is simply a relationship between the coordinates. In this case also a single constraint condition reduces the number of degrees of freedom by one.

Where a system consists of more than two particles, the same results obtain: the number of degrees of freedom is equal to the total number of possible degrees of freedom less the number of constraints. If there are n degrees of freedom any configuration can be described by a set of n coordinates. These n coordinates can be chosen in many ways, but any one set can always be obtained from any other.

It is often convenient in dynamical analysis to refer to a set of coordinates of a system without specifying in any way the manner in which the coordinates are to be defined, or even what system we are to consider. In order to do this we adopt a quite general notation and refer to our coordinates not as x, y, z or r, θ, ϕ but as $q_1, q_2, \ldots, q_n$. These are known as *generalised coordinates*. Use of the term is normally restricted to a set of n independent coordinates necessary to specify unambiguously all configurations of an n-degree-of-freedom system. More orthodox descriptions of the displacements of a system can always be determined in terms of any set of generalised coordinates: if the position of the ith particle is denoted by the position vector $\mathbf{r}_i$ this can be expressed in terms of the q_j by a relationship of the form

$$\mathbf{r}_i = \mathbf{r}_i(q_1, q_2, \ldots, q_n). \tag{1}$$

It is natural also to make use of generalised velocities and accelerations, which are simply the time differentials of the generalised coordinates:

$$\dot{q}_1, \dot{q}_2, \ldots, \ddot{q}_1, \ddot{q}_2, \ldots \, .$$

The forces occurring in dynamical problems can conveniently be divided into three classes: constraint forces, applied forces, and inertia forces.

(*a*) *Constraint Forces.* Although a constraint is a kinematical restriction, it can only be imposed by the action of a force, or forces. Thus there is tension or compression in an inextensible connection between two moving particles, and a reaction force where a particle is constrained to move on a surface. These are real forces and must not be ignored: they have one important property in common in that they do no work in any small displacement.

(b) *Applied Forces.* Under this heading we include all real forces which are not constraint forces, i.e. all forces which do work when the system is displaced.

(c) *Inertia Forces.* Inertia forces are the reversed effective forces necessary to convert a dynamical problem into a statical form. (The effective force on a particle is the product of its mass and its acceleration.)

If we are to set up equations of motion in terms of generalised coordinates $q_1, q_2, \ldots$, which may be arbitrarily chosen, the forces acting on the system must be included as *generalised forces* Q_1, $Q_2, \ldots$, defined such that the q's and the Q's correspond in a particular sense.

Suppose that forces $\mathbf{P}_i$ act at a number of points at positions $\mathbf{r}_i$ which have displacements $\delta\mathbf{r}_i$; then the work done by the forces, which we may denote by δW, is given by

$$\delta W = \sum_i \mathbf{P}_i \cdot \delta\mathbf{r}_i. \tag{2}$$

The generalised forces Q_j are defined such that in the same displacement the same quantity δW is given by

$$\delta W = \sum_j Q_j \, \delta q_j; \tag{3}$$

so by expressing the changes in the generalised coordinates q_j in terms of those of the coordinates of the $\mathbf{r}_i$, the Q_j can be defined to represent any known set of forces $\mathbf{P}_i$. (We shall keep the subscript j to indicate a typical generalised coordinate and the other generalised quantities corresponding to it: the subscript i can then be used for a typical point or particle.)

Because they do no work the constraint forces can have no influence on the generalised forces; consequently analysis in terms of generalised forces will never need specifically to include constraint forces.

Use of the symbol δW to indicate a quantity of work does not necessarily indicate the existence of a definable large quantity W. In certain cases, however, forces do give rise to a potential energy V, and then $\delta W = -\delta V$. (The need for the minus sign is obvious if we note that a particle moved in the direction of its weight experiences a *loss* of potential energy.) In such a case

$$\delta V = -\sum_j Q_j \, \delta q_j,$$

and as $\qquad \delta V = \dfrac{\partial V}{\partial q_1} \delta q_1 + \dfrac{\partial V}{\partial q_2} \delta q_2 + \dots ,$

we see by comparing coefficients that $Q_j = -\dfrac{\partial V}{\partial q_j}.$ \qquad (4)

We are now in a position to state Lagrange's equations, which we shall do without proof.

For a system of n degrees of freedom, of which $q_1, q_2, \dots, q_n$ are any complete set of generalised coordinates and $Q_1, Q_2, \dots, Q_n$ are the corresponding generalised forces, the following n equations apply:

$$\frac{d}{dt}\left(\frac{\partial T}{\partial \dot{q}_j}\right) - \frac{\partial T}{\partial q_j} + \frac{\partial V}{\partial q_j} = Q_j, \qquad (5)$$
$$(j = 1, 2, \dots, n),$$

where T and V are respectively the kinetic and potential energies expressed in terms of the $q_j, \dot{q}_j$.

These equations describe the motion of any system completely, in terms of any set of generalised coordinates. It may be noted that all the inertia forces are included in the T terms: all constraint forces vanish. All applied forces can be included in the Q_j, but if they have potential it is usually more convenient to include them in the V terms.

A.4 Theory of Small Vibrations

In considering the vibration of a mechanical system it is usually possible to restrict our attention to small motions. If, in such a case, we choose coordinates which are zero in the equilibrium configuration, the equations of motion can be simplified greatly and important general results emerge.

Let $q_1, q_2, \dots, q_n$ be a set of generalised coordinates chosen to be zero in the equilibrium configuration, and let the motion be such that they remain small.

Then V will be a quadratic expression in the q_j. Higher powers will be negligible if the q_j are small: terms independent of the q_j can be ignored because the datum from which V is measured is arbitrary, and accordingly only the differential of V appears in the equations: terms linear in the q_j would on differentiation give constants and so violate the necessary condition $\partial V/\partial q_j = 0$ at the equilibrium position where all the q_j are zero. We may therefore write

$$V = \tfrac{1}{2}(c_{11} q_1{}^2 + c_{22} q_2{}^2 + \ldots + 2c_{12} q_1 q_2 + \ldots), \qquad (1)$$

where c_{11}, c_{12}, etc., are constants.

We can show also that T will be a quadratic expression in the $\dot{q}_j$:

as $T = \sum_i \tfrac{1}{2} m_i \dot{\mathbf{r}}_i{}^2$ and $\dot{\mathbf{r}}_i = \dfrac{\partial \mathbf{r}_i}{\partial q_1} \dot{q}_1 + \dfrac{\partial \mathbf{r}_i}{\partial q_2} \dot{q}_2 + \ldots,$

we may write $T = \tfrac{1}{2}(a_{11} \dot{q}_1{}^2 + a_{22} \dot{q}_2{}^2 + \ldots + 2a_{12} \dot{q}_1 \dot{q}_2 + \ldots), \quad (2)$
and although the a_{rs} are seen to be functions of the q_j, they can be assumed constant if the q_j are small enough.

Applying Lagrange's equations in the form

$$\frac{d}{dt}\left(\frac{\partial T}{\partial \dot{q}_j}\right) - \frac{\partial T}{\partial q_j} + \frac{\partial V}{\partial q_j} = Q_j, \qquad (3)$$

$$(j = 1, 2, \ldots, n),$$

and neglecting damping, we obtain a set of n equations of motion in the form

$$\left.\begin{array}{l} (a_{11} \ddot{q}_1 + a_{12} \ddot{q}_2 + \ldots) + (c_{11} q_1 + c_{12} q_2 + \ldots) = Q_1, \\ (a_{21} \ddot{q}_1 + a_{22} \ddot{q}_2 + \ldots) + (c_{21} q_1 + c_{22} q_2 + \ldots) = Q_2, \\ \quad \cdot \quad\quad \cdot \quad\quad\quad\quad\quad\quad \cdot \quad\quad\quad \cdot \\ (a_{n1} \ddot{q}_1 + a_{n2} \ddot{q}_2 + \ldots) + (c_{n1} q_1 + c_{n2} q_2 + \ldots) = Q_n, \end{array}\right\} \quad (4)$$

where the Q_j are the generalised forces corresponding to the q_j.

(Here a_{21} is actually equal to a_{12}, etc: distinction between the two is made only for the sake of symmetry.)

Equations (4) are the general equations of motion for small displacements of a system having n degrees of freedom in the absence of damping.

A.5 Normal Modes

Where no external forces act the Q_j are zero and A.4(4) become

$$
\left.
\begin{aligned}
&(a_{11}\ddot{q}_1 + a_{12}\ddot{q}_2 + \ldots) + (c_{11}q_1 + c_{12}q_2 + \ldots) = 0, \\
&(a_{21}\ddot{q}_1 + a_{22}\ddot{q}_2 + \ldots) + (c_{21}q_1 + c_{22}q_2 + \ldots) = 0, \\
&\;\cdot\quad\cdot\quad\cdot\quad\cdot\quad\cdot\quad\cdot\quad\cdot\quad\cdot\quad\cdot\quad\cdot\quad\cdot \\
&(a_{n1}\ddot{q}_1 + a_{n2}\ddot{q}_2 + \ldots) + (c_{n1}q_1 + c_{n2}q_2 + \ldots) = 0.
\end{aligned}
\right\} \quad (1)
$$

By inspection we see that

$$
q_1 = \hat{q}_1 \sin \omega t,\; q_2 = \hat{q}_2 \sin \omega t,\; \ldots,\; q_n = \hat{q}_n \sin \omega t, \quad (2)
$$

is a solution: substituting in (1) we have

$$
\left.
\begin{aligned}
&(-\omega^2 a_{11} + c_{11})\hat{q}_1 + (-\omega^2 a_{12} + c_{12})\hat{q}_2 + \ldots = 0, \\
&(-\omega^2 a_{21} + c_{21})\hat{q}_1 + (-\omega^2 a_{22} + c_{22})\hat{q}_2 + \ldots = 0, \\
&\;\cdot\quad\cdot\quad\cdot\quad\cdot\quad\cdot\quad\cdot\quad\cdot\quad\cdot\quad\cdot\quad\cdot \\
&(-\omega^2 a_{n1} + c_{n1})\hat{q}_1 + (-\omega^2 a_{n2} + c_{n2})\hat{q}_2 + \ldots = 0,
\end{aligned}
\right\} \quad (3)
$$

which are a set of n simultaneous equation in the $\hat{q}_j$.

Sets of equations such as (3) are known to have non-trivial solutions only for certain particular values of ω^2, (the so-called *eigenvalues*) such that the determinant formed from the coefficients of the equations vanishes. There are thus non-trivial solutions only when

$$
\begin{vmatrix}
-\omega^2 a_{11} + c_{11}, & -\omega^2 a_{12} + c_{12}, & \ldots \\
-\omega^2 a_{21} + c_{21}, & -\omega^2 a_{22} + c_{22}, & \ldots \\
\cdot & \cdot & \cdot \\
-\omega^2 a_{n1} + c_{n1}, & -\omega^2 a_{n2} + c_{n2}, & \ldots
\end{vmatrix} = 0. \quad (4)
$$

This equation is of degree n in ω^2 and it can be shown that all roots are real and positive. There are thus n frequencies at which our assumed solution is valid: we shall denote these by ω_I, ω_{II}, ω_{III}, $\ldots$ etc.

If we solve (4) for ω^2 and substitute any particular root ω_I^2 in (3) we shall obtain from it a particular set of $\hat{q}_j$ each bearing a definite ratio to each other. One solution of (1) is therefore

$$
q_1 = \hat{q}_{1I} \sin \omega_I t,\; q_2 = \hat{q}_{2I} \sin \omega_I t,\; \ldots,\; q_n = \hat{q}_{nI} \sin \omega_I t, \quad (5)
$$

where the amplitudes have a definite ratio $(\hat{q}_1 : \hat{q}_2 : \ldots : \hat{q}_n)_I$, and where all motions are clearly in phase, or exactly out of phase, with frequency ω_I.

A second root of (4), ω_{II}^2, gives

$$q_1 = \hat{q}_{1II} \sin \omega_{II} t, \; q_2 = \hat{q}_{2II} \sin \omega_{II} t, \ldots, q_n = \hat{q}_{nII} \sin \omega_{II} t, \quad (6)$$

where the amplitudes have a ratio $(\hat{q}_1 : \hat{q}_2 : \ldots : \hat{q}_n)_{II}$, and all motions have frequency ω_{II}. And so on for all the other roots of (4).

Solutions such as (5) and (6) in which all coordinates vary harmonically, in phase, at some particular frequency, are all possible free motions of the undamped system. The frequencies ω_I, ω_{II}, etc., are the *natural frequencies* of the system: the corresponding ratios $(\hat{q}_1 : \hat{q}_2 : \ldots : \hat{q}_n)_I$, $(\hat{q}_1 : \hat{q}_2 : \ldots : \hat{q}_n)_{II}$, etc., are called the *normal modes* (or principal modes) of the system. In many systems the generalised coordinates are many and have a clear geometrical significance: the normal modes then define the shape of the vibration form at the particular frequency.

The fact that vibration in a normal mode at a single natural frequency is a possible free motion does not mean that it is likely to occur in practice. The general solution of (1) clearly must contain contributions from all normal mode solutions, and a free vibration will in general take the form

$$
\left.
\begin{aligned}
q_1 &= \hat{q}_{1I} \sin (\omega_I t + \phi_I) + \hat{q}_{1II} \sin (\omega_{II} t + \phi_{II}) + \ldots \\
&\qquad\qquad\qquad\qquad + \hat{q}_{1N} \sin (\omega_N t + \phi_N), \\
q_2 &= \hat{q}_{2I} \sin (\omega_I t + \phi_I) + \hat{q}_{2II} \sin (\omega_{II} t + \phi_{II}) + \ldots \\
&\qquad\qquad\qquad\qquad + \hat{q}_{2N} \sin (\omega_N t + \phi_N), \\
\cdot\;\;&\;\;\cdot\;\;\;\;\cdot\;\;\;\;\cdot\;\;\;\;\cdot\;\;\;\;\cdot\;\;\;\;\cdot\;\;\;\;\cdot\;\;\;\;\cdot \\
q_n &= \hat{q}_{nI} \sin (\omega_I t + \phi_I) + \hat{q}_{nII} \sin (\omega_{II} t + \phi_{II}) + \ldots \\
&\qquad\qquad\qquad\qquad + \hat{q}_{nN} \sin (\omega_N t + \phi_N).
\end{aligned}
\right\} \quad (7)
$$

The general solution (7) is somewhat complicated, but so, indeed, is the free motion of a vibrating system. It becomes much easier to comprehend if we consider it not as a set of n^2 terms but as a summation of n simple harmonic motions. This simplification forms the basis of normal mode analysis.

A.6 Normal Coordinates

Consider a freely vibrating system of n degrees of freedom. Using any set of generalised coordinates $q_1, q_2, \ldots, q_n$ we can express the kinetic and potential energies as

$$
\left.
\begin{aligned}
T &= \tfrac{1}{2}(a_{11} \dot{q}_1^2 + a_{22} \dot{q}_2^2 + \ldots + 2a_{12} \dot{q}_1 \dot{q}_2 + \ldots), \\
V &= \tfrac{1}{2}(c_{11} q_1^2 + c_{22} q_2^2 + \ldots + 2c_{12} q_1 q_2 + \ldots).
\end{aligned}
\right\} \quad (1)
$$

Using Lagrange's equations, we have equations of motion given by:

$$\left.\begin{array}{l} a_{11}\ddot{q}_1 + c_{11}q_1 + a_{12}\ddot{q}_2 + c_{12}q_2 + \ldots = 0, \\ a_{21}\ddot{q}_1 + c_{21}q_1 + a_{22}\ddot{q}_2 + c_{22}q_2 + \ldots = 0, \\ \ \cdot\quad\cdot\quad\cdot\quad\cdot\quad\cdot\quad\cdot\quad\cdot\quad\cdot \\ a_{n1}\ddot{q}_1 + c_{n1}q_1 + a_{n2}\ddot{q}_2 + c_{n2}q_2 + \ldots = 0. \end{array}\right\} \quad (2)$$

All the generalised coordinates appear in all the equations (2), in general, so that there is always *coupling* between the coordinates: a change in one coordinate does not occur without changes in the others.

The coupling terms may be seen to arise from the product terms in (1). But we can show that there can always be found a set of generalised coordinates, which we shall denote by $\xi_1, \xi_2, \ldots, \xi_n$, such that there are no product terms in the expressions for T and V. When such is the case, coupling cannot occur.

For small displacements, any set of generalised coordinates can be expressed in terms of any other by a linear transformation; i.e.

$$\left.\begin{array}{l} q_1 = d_{11}\xi_1 + d_{12}\xi_2 + \ldots + d_{1n}\xi_n, \\ q_2 = d_{21}\xi_1 + d_{22}\xi_2 + \ldots + d_{2n}\xi_n, \\ \ \cdot\quad\cdot\quad\ \cdot\quad\cdot\quad\cdot\quad\cdot\quad\cdot \\ q_n = d_{n1}\xi_1 + d_{n2}\xi_2 + \ldots + d_{nn}\xi_n. \end{array}\right\} \quad (3)$$

We can choose the n^2 coefficients d_{rs} in any way and can certainly satisfy the condition that the (n^2-n) coefficients a_{rs}, c_{rs}, of the product terms in (1) are zero.

If this is done, we have

$$\left.\begin{array}{l} T = \tfrac{1}{2}(a_1\dot{\xi}_1{}^2 + a_2\dot{\xi}_2{}^2 + \ldots + a_n\dot{\xi}_n{}^2), \\ V = \tfrac{1}{2}(c_1\xi_1{}^2 + c_2\xi_2{}^2 + \ldots + c_n\xi_n{}^2), \end{array}\right\} \quad (4)$$

and so, applying Lagrange's equations, we obtain

$$\left.\begin{array}{l} a_1\ddot{\xi}_1 + c_1\xi_1 = 0, \\ a_2\ddot{\xi}_2 + c_2\xi_2 = 0, \\ \ \cdot\quad\cdot\quad\cdot\quad\cdot\quad\cdot\quad\cdot \\ a_n\ddot{\xi}_n + c_n\xi_n = 0. \end{array}\right\} \quad (5)$$

Each separate equation is now identical to that obtained for a simple spring-mass system.

Each equation of (5) has its own solution with its own natural frequency, $\omega_r = \sqrt{(c_r/a_r)}$ and the value of each ξ_r represents the contribution of the rth normal mode. In general all ξ_r will exist, but if the motion consists of single normal mode only one ξ_r is other than zero. Such ξ_r are known as *normal* (or principal) *coordinates*.

Suppose a system to be vibrating in, say, its 1st normal mode. Then $\xi_2 = \xi_3 = \ldots = \xi_n = 0$, and from (3) we see that

$$\left.\begin{aligned}
q_1 &= d_{11}\,\xi_1, \\
q_2 &= d_{21}\,\xi_1, \\
\cdot\ \ \cdot\ \ \cdot\ \ \cdot\ \ \cdot \\
q_n &= d_{n1}\,\xi_1.
\end{aligned}\right\} \tag{6}$$

Thus the ratio $(\hat{q}_1 : \hat{q}_2 : \ldots : \hat{q}_n)_I = (d_{11} : d_{21} : \ldots : d_{n1})$, so that the ratio of the d's in any one 'column' of (3) gives the shape of the normal mode corresponding to its ξ_r.

The definition given here of normal coordinates is arbitrary to the extent of allowing multiplication of each by any constant factor: provided that the ratio of the d's in any column of (3) represents a normal mode, the ξ_r will be normal coordinates.

So far we have considered only free vibration. Had there been external forces there would have been Q_j on the right-hand sides of (2), and so generalised forces Ξ_r on the right-hand sides of (5), defined such that $\sum_j Q_j\,\delta q_j = \sum_r \Xi_r\,\delta\xi_r$; each equation of (5) would then represent forced vibration in one of the normal modes. Often the generalised vocabulary is extended further to refer to the coefficients $a_1, a_2, \ldots$, as generalised masses.

A.7 The Effects of Damping

The effects of damping, which we have hitherto neglected, can be allowed for in Lagrange's equations either by inserting suitable Q_j on the right-hand sides, or by adding terms $\dfrac{\partial F}{\partial \dot{q}_j}$ on the left-hand sides (where F is a quantity called the *Dissipation Function*). As F can be shown to be similar in form to the kinetic energy T, it can for small motions be expanded in the same way, and so

$$F = \tfrac{1}{2}(b_{11}\,\dot{q}_1{}^2 + b_{22}\,\dot{q}_2{}^2 + \ldots + 2b_{12}\,\dot{q}_1\,\dot{q}_2 + \ldots) \tag{1}$$

for a system having n degrees of freedom. Again when the terms q_j are small the coefficients b_{rs} can be considered constant.

Using Lagrange's equations, with the term $\dfrac{\partial F}{\partial \dot{q}_j}$ included on the left-hand side, we obtain equations of motion of the form

$$
\left.
\begin{aligned}
a_{11}\ddot{q}_1 + a_{12}\ddot{q}_2 + \ldots + b_{11}\dot{q}_1 + b_{12}\dot{q}_2 + \ldots + c_{11}q_1 + c_{12}q_2 + \ldots \\
= Q_1, \\
a_{21}\ddot{q}_1 + a_{22}\ddot{q}_2 + \ldots + b_{21}\dot{q}_1 + b_{22}\dot{q}_2 + \ldots + c_{21}q_1 + c_{22}q_2 + \ldots \\
= Q_2, \\
\cdot \quad \cdot \quad \cdot \quad \cdot \quad \cdot \quad \cdot \quad \cdot \quad \cdot \quad \cdot \quad \cdot \quad \cdot \quad \cdot \quad \cdot \\
a_{n1}\ddot{q}_1 + a_{n2}\ddot{q}_2 + \ldots + b_{n1}\dot{q}_1 + b_{n2}\dot{q}_2 + \ldots + c_{n1}q_1 + c_{n2}q_2 + \ldots \\
= Q_n.
\end{aligned}
\right\} \quad (2)
$$

As we have seen, it is always possible to express T and V without product terms by use of normal coordinates. But it is not in general possible at the same time to express F without product terms, and the equations of motion will, in general, be of the form:

$$
a_1\ddot{\xi}_1 + (b'_{11}\dot{\xi}_1 + b'_{12}\dot{\xi}_2 + \ldots) + c_1\xi_1 = \Xi_1, \text{ etc.} \quad (3)
$$

If, however, damping is small, it is often permissible to neglect the coupling effect arising from the product terms, in which case the equations of motion are effectively

$$
a_r\ddot{\xi}_r + b_r\dot{\xi}_r + c_r\xi_r = \Xi_r, \quad (4)
$$
$$
(r = 1, 2, \ldots, n).
$$

Again each equation is identical in form to that obtained for a simple spring-mass system, so that the solutions of Section A.2 apply.

If a hysteretic damping model is preferred, and if the Ξ_r are, or are nearly, harmonic, then (4) can be modified in the obvious way to give

$$
a_r\ddot{\xi}_r + c_r(1 + i\eta_r)\xi_r = \Xi_r, \quad (5)
$$
$$
(r = 1, 2, \ldots, n).
$$

A.8 Response in Terms of Normal Modes

The use of normal-mode analysis is best illustrated by means of a simple example: we shall therefore consider here the motion of a beam of which the normal modes and natural frequencies are assumed known. We shall at first neglect damping.

Let the displacement of the beam at any time be given by

$$
w(x, t) = \sum_r \xi_r(t)\, w_r(x), \quad (1)
$$

where $w_r(x)$ represents the deflexion form of the rth normal mode.

RV K

(We can assume on the basis of experience that this series converges.) Equation (1) corresponds exactly to equations A.6(3), and would in fact look identical to it if a separate equation were to be written for each successive value of x. The $\xi_r(t)$ are thus normal coordinates. Lagrange's equations in the form

$$\frac{d}{dt}\left(\frac{\partial T}{\partial \dot{\xi}_r}\right)+\frac{\partial V}{\partial \xi_r} = \Xi_r, \quad (r = 1, 2, \ldots), \tag{2}$$

can be used if we first express T and V in terms of the ξ_r.

We have

$$T = \int_0^l \tfrac{1}{2}\, \dot{w}^2(x, t)\, m\, dx,$$

$$= \tfrac{1}{2} \int_0^l \left[\sum_r \dot{\xi}_r\, w_r(x)\right]^2 m\, dx,$$

$$= \tfrac{1}{2} \int_0^l \sum_r \dot{\xi}_r^2\, w_r^2(x)\, m\, dx,$$

because the product terms of normal coordinates do not exist,

$$= \sum_r \tfrac{1}{2} M_r\, \dot{\xi}_r^2, \tag{3}$$

where the generalised mass $M_r = \displaystyle\int_0^l w_r^2(x)\, m\, dx$.

Thus $$\frac{d}{dt}\left(\frac{\partial T}{\partial \dot{\xi}_r}\right) = M_r\, \ddot{\xi}_r. \tag{4}$$

The potential energy V could be determined in the same way, but this is unnecessary if the natural frequencies ω_r are available. Clearly equations (2) with $\Xi_r = 0$ must give the separate normal mode equations for free vibration, i.e. $\ddot{\xi}_r+\omega_r^2\, \xi_r = 0$; as the first term of (2) gives $M_r\, \ddot{\xi}_r$ the second term must give $M_r\, \omega_r^2\, \xi_r$. This must also give the value of the second term in the present case when $\Xi_r \neq 0$.

Lagrange's equations therefore give

$$M_r\, \ddot{\xi}_r+\omega_r^2\, M_r\, \xi_r = \Xi_r, \tag{5}$$
$$(r = 1, 2, \ldots).$$

Equations (5) can always be solved for the ξ_r, and substitution in

(1) then gives $w(x, t)$ completely. This splitting up of the problem into simple equations for the separate modes obviously makes its solution much simpler.

An example will show this. Suppose that the beam is subject to a force $P = \hat{P} \cos \omega t$ at the point $x = x_P$.

$$\text{Then} \qquad \sum_r \Xi_r \, \delta\xi_r = \delta W = P \, \delta w(x_P, t)$$

$$= P \sum_r w_r(x_P) \, \delta\xi_r :$$

thus $\qquad \Xi_r = \hat{\Xi}_r \cos \omega t = w_r(x_P) \, \hat{P} \cos \omega t. \qquad (6)$

So solving (5) for this loading,

$$\xi_r = \hat{\xi}_r \cos \omega t = \frac{\hat{\Xi}_r \cos \omega t}{M_r(\omega_r{}^2 - \omega^2)}, \qquad (7)$$

and therefore $\qquad w(x, t) = \sum_r \frac{\hat{P} \, w_r(x_P) \, w_r(x)}{M_r(\omega_r{}^2 - \omega^2)} \cos \omega t. \qquad (8)$

Near any resonance frequency a single term of the summation will obviously predominate.

In the above we have not needed to pay attention to the absolute magnitudes of the $w_r(x)$: if for example $w_r(x) = \sin \dfrac{r\pi x}{l}$, we could have used $w_r(x) = a \sin \dfrac{r\pi x}{l}$ instead. Examination of (8) shows that any such factor a affects numerator and denominator equally, for M_r contains $w_r{}^2(x)$: if we double w_r, we simply double Ξ_r, and so halve ξ_r.

Extension to more complicated systems presents no difficulty in principle.

The presence of damping, if small, would have modified this analysis slightly. We can easily indicate the extent of this modification: let us assume that in the example considered here the damping was hysteretic, and such as to cause no appreciable coupling between the modes.

Equations (5) would now become

$$M_r \ddot{\xi}_r + \omega_r{}^2 \, M_r(1 + i\eta_r) \, \xi_r = \Xi_r, \qquad (9)$$
$$(r = 1, 2, \ldots):$$

Ξ_r would now be expressed as $\hat{\Xi}_r \, e^{i\omega t}$, it being assumed that the exciting force was $P = \hat{P} \, e^{i\omega t}$ as in A.2(4).

Solving for $\xi_r = \hat{\xi}_r\, e^{i\omega t}$ would now give

$$\hat{\xi}_r = \frac{\hat{\Xi}_r}{M_r(\omega_r^2 - \omega^2 + i\eta_r\omega_r^2)}, \tag{10}$$

and so
$$w(x, t) = \sum_r \frac{\hat{P}\, w_r(x_P)\, w_r(x)}{M_r(\omega_r^2 - \omega^2 + i\eta_r\omega_r^2)}\, e^{i\omega t}, \tag{11}$$

where we have to take the real part to obtain the actual response. Again the total response is a summation of the responses in the single normal modes (added with regard to phase, of course): again if damping is small a single term will predominate at or near any resonance frequency.

The complex receptance $\alpha_{1P}(i\omega)$ corresponding to A.2(9), defining the displacement $w(x_1, t)$ at any point $x = x_1$ due to a harmonically varying force P, is easily obtainable from (11):

$$\alpha_{1P}(i\omega) = \sum_r \frac{w_r(x_P)\, w_r(x_1)}{M_r(\omega_r^2 - \omega^2 + i\eta_r\omega_r^2)}. \tag{12}$$

A.9 Orthogonality and Initial Conditions

We have already, in obtaining A.8(3), used the fact that when T and V are expressed in terms of the normal coordinates the product terms vanish. The condition that the coefficient of a product term vanishes is worth stating explicitly as it has useful applications.

Consider the beam of the previous section, and suppose that its motion is such that only two normal modes – the rth and the sth – are present. Then the displacement is given by

$$w(x, t) = w_r(x)\, \xi_r(t) + w_s(x)\, \xi_s(t). \tag{1}$$

The kinetic energy T is given by

$$T = \tfrac{1}{2} \int_0^l \dot{w}^2(x, t)\, m\, dx$$

$$= \tfrac{1}{2}\left[\dot{\xi}_r^2 \int_0^l w_r^2(x)\, m\, dx + 2\dot{\xi}_r\dot{\xi}_s \int_0^l w_r(x)\, w_s(x)\, m\, dx \right.$$

$$\left. + \dot{\xi}_s^2 \int_0^l w_s^2(x)\, m\, dx \right].$$

If the product term vanishes, as it must at all times, it must be the case that

$$\int_0^l w_r(x)\, w_s(x)\, m\, dx = 0, \quad \text{for } r \neq s, \tag{2}$$

and this result is in no way affected if other modes are present also. Equation (2) is known as the condition of *orthogonality* of normal modes.

A similar result can be obtained for any other elastic body if suitable symbols are introduced: in fact if the points of the body are defined relative to some origin by the vector **p**, and the normal mode displacement by $\mathbf{u}_r(\mathbf{p})$, the condition of orthogonality becomes

$$\int \mathbf{u}_r(\mathbf{p}) \cdot \mathbf{u}_s(\mathbf{p})\, dm = 0, \quad \text{for } r \neq s, \tag{3}$$

the integral being taken over all mass elements dm of the body.

The orthogonality condition can be used very conveniently to establish the initial conditions of the normal coordinates corresponding to known initial conditions of the physical coordinates. This we can demonstrate by considering the beam problem again.

Let us determine the weighting function $W(t)$ giving the displacement at any point x of a beam of length l and mass per unit length m due to an impulsive transverse loading $I\,\delta(t)$ applied at the point $x = x_I$. We shall assume here that damping is viscous and small. We can assume that the beam is initially at rest in its equilibrium position.

Let us write as before

$$w(x, t) = \sum_r \xi_r(t)\, w_r(x), \tag{4}$$

where the $w_r(x)$ are the normal modes, and the $\xi_r(t)$ are normal coordinates. Then the equations of motion in terms of the $\xi_r(t)$ will be

$$\ddot{\xi}_r + 2\Delta_r\, \dot{\xi}_r + \omega_r^2\, \xi_r = 0, \tag{5}$$
$$(r = 1, 2, \ldots),$$

where Δ_r is the damping constant in the rth normal mode and ω_r is the rth natural frequency. We assume that there is no coupling due to damping.

In order to solve (5) we must be able to specify the initial conditions for each separate ξ_r from our knowledge of $w(x, 0)$, $\dot{w}(x, 0)$.

If we multiply both sides of equation (4) by $m\, w_r(x)$ and integrate over the length of the beam we have, because of the orthogonality property

$$\int_0^l w_r(x)\, w(x, t)\, m\, dx = \xi_r(t) \int_0^l w_r(x)\, w_r(x)\, m\, dx$$
$$= M_r\, \xi_r(t),$$

where $M_r = \displaystyle\int_0^l w_r^2(x)\, m\, dx$ is the rth generalised mass.

So

$$\xi_r(t) = \frac{1}{M_r} \int_0^l w_r(x)\, w(x, t)\, m\, dx,$$

and

$$\dot{\xi}_r(t) = \frac{1}{M_r} \int_0^l w_r(x)\, \dot{w}(x, t)\, m\, dx. \tag{6}$$

Now the initial conditions are:

(i) $w(x, 0) = 0$ throughout,

(ii) $w(x, 0) = 0$, except in a small part of the beam, δm, close to the point $x = x_I$, in which the momentum $\delta m\, \dot{w}(x_I, 0)$ must be equal to the impulse I.

Substituting in (6), we have

$$\xi_r(0) = 0,$$
$$\dot{\xi}_r(0) = \frac{1}{M_r}\, w_r(x_I)\, \frac{I}{\delta m}\, \delta m = \frac{I\, w_r(x_I)}{M_r}. \tag{7}$$

Solving (5) and choosing the constants to satisfy (7) gives

$$\xi_r = \frac{I\, w_r(x_I)}{\omega_r'\, M_r}\, e^{-\Delta_r t} \sin \omega_r' t, \tag{8}$$
$$\text{where } \omega_r'^2 = \omega_r^2 - \Delta_r^2.$$

So the complete solution is

$$w(x, t) = \sum_r w_r(x)\, \xi_r(t)$$
$$= I \sum_r \frac{w_r(x_I)\, w_r(x)}{\omega_r'\, M_r}\, e^{-\Delta_r t} \sin \omega_r' t, \tag{9}$$

and the required weighting function is of the form

$$W(t) = \sum A_r\, e^{-\Delta_r t} \sin \omega_r' t, \tag{10}$$

$$\text{with } A_r = \frac{w_r(x_I)\, w_r(x)}{\omega_r'\, M_r^4}.$$

BIBLIOGRAPHY

This bibliography has been provided primarily in order that references in the text might easily be made. A few books and papers have been included for other reasons such as their importance in the subject, or because they represent directions of work which the reader may wish to follow, so that the subject is covered to some extent, but there is no pretence of completeness. Extensive bibliographies are to be found elsewhere, in references 1 and 9 for example.

The basic ideas of random processes are treated in references 1, 11, 15; reference 8 contains the lecture notes of an M.I.T. Summer Programme on Random Vibration. Rice's long paper (reference 21) is of fundamental importance.

1 BENDAT, J. S. *Principles and Applications of Random Noise Theory*, Wiley, 1958.
2 BISHOP, R. E. D. & JOHNSON, D. C. *The Mechanics of Vibration*, Cambridge University Press, 1960.
3 BLACKMAN, R. B. & TUKEY, J. W. The Measurement of Power Spectra, *Bell System Tech. Journal*, Vol. 37, pp. 185-282, 485-569, 1958.
4 BOGDANOFF, J. L. & GOLDBERG, J. E. On the Bernoulli-Euler Beam Theory With Random Excitation, *J. Aero/Space Sci.*, Vol. 27, pp. 371-376, 1960.
5 CLARKSON, B. L. The Design of Structures to Resist Jet Noise Fatigue, *J. Roy. Aero. Soc.*, Vol. 66, pp. 603-613, 1962.
6 CLARKSON, B. L. & FORD, R. D. The Response of a Typical Aircraft Structure to Jet Noise, *J. Roy. Aero. Soc.*, Vol. 66, pp. 31-40, 1962.
7 CRAMER, H. *The Elements of Probability Theory*, Wiley, 1955.
8 CRANDALL, S. H. (ed.) *Random Vibration*, Technology Press/Wiley, 1958.
9 CRANDALL, S. H. Random Vibration, *Appl. Mech. Rev.*, Vol. 12, pp. 739-742, 1959.
10 CRANDALL, S. H. & YILDIZ, A. Random Vibration of Beams, *J. Appl. Mech.*, Vol. 29, pp. 267-275, 1962.

11   DAVENPORT, W. B. & ROOT, W. L. *An Introduction to the Theory of Random Signals and Noise*, McGraw-Hill, 1958.

12   ERINGEN, A. C. Response of Beams and Plates to Random Loads, *J. Appl. Mech.*, Vol. 24, pp. 46-52, 1957.

13   JAHNKE, E. & EMDE, F. *Tables of Functions with Formulae and Curves*, (4th Ed.), Dover, 1945.

14   JAMES, H. F., NICHOLS, N. B. & PHILLIPS, R. S. *Theory of Servomechanisms*, McGraw-Hill, 1947.

15   LANING, J. H. & BATTIN, R. H. *Random Processes in Automatic Control*, McGraw-Hill, 1956.

16   LYON, R. H. Response of Strings to Random Noise Fields, *J. Acoust. Soc. Am.* Vol. 28, pp. 391-398, 1956.

17   MILES, J. W. On Structural Fatigue under Random Loading, *J. Aero. Sci.* Vol. 21, pp. 753-762, 1954.

18   MINER, M. A. Cumulative Damage in Fatigue, *J. Appl. Mech.*, Vol. 12, A159-A164, 1945.

19   POWELL, A. On the Fatigue Failure of Structures due to Vibrations Excited by Random Pressure Fields, *J. Acoust. Soc. Am.*, Vol. 30, pp. 1130-1135.

20   RAYLEIGH, LORD. *The Theory of Sound*, (2nd Ed.), Macmillan, London, 1894.

21   RICE, S. O. Mathematical Analysis of Random Noise, *Bell System Tech. Journal*, Vol. 23, pp. 282-332, 1944 and vol. 24, pp. 46-156, 1945. See also WAX (in which this is to be found).

22   TACK, D. H. & LAMBERT, R. F. Response of Bars and Plates to Boundary-Layer Turbulence, *J. Aerospace Sci.*, Vol. 29, pp. 311-322, 1962.

23   THOMSON, W. T. & BARTON, M. V. The Response of Mechanical Systems to Random Excitation, *J. Appl. Mech.*, Vol. 24, pp. 248-251, 1957.

24   TIMOSHENKO, S. P. & YOUNG, D. H. *Advanced Dynamics*, (4th Ed.), McGraw-Hill, 1956.

25   WAX, N. (ed.) *Selected Papers on Noise and Stochastic Processes*, Dover, 1954. (Includes Reference 21.)

INDEX

INDEX